FE

chemical
practice exam

978-1-947801-03-5

ISBN 978-1-947801-03-5

Printed in the United States of America
1st printing January 2020

CONTENTS

About NCEES

NCEES is a nonprofit organization made up of the U.S. engineering and surveying licensing boards in all 50 states, U.S. territories, and the District of Columbia. We develop and score the exams used for engineering and surveying licensure in the United States. NCEES also promotes professional mobility through its services for licensees and its member boards.

Engineering licensure in the United States is regulated by licensing boards in each state and territory. These boards set and maintain the standards that protect the public they serve. As a result, licensing requirements and procedures vary by jurisdiction, so stay in touch with your board (ncees.org/licensing-boards).

Exam Format

The FE exam contains 110 questions and is administered year-round via computer at approved Pearson VUE test centers. A 6-hour appointment time includes a tutorial, the exam, and a break. You'll have 5 hours and 20 minutes to complete the actual exam.

In addition to traditional multiple-choice questions with one correct answer, the FE exam uses common alternative item types such as

- Multiple correct options—allows multiple choices to be correct
- Point and click—requires examinees to click on part of a graphic to answer
- Drag and drop—requires examinees to click on and drag items to match, sort, rank, or label
- Fill in the blank—provides a space for examinees to enter a response to the question

To familiarize yourself with the format, style, and navigation of a computer-based exam, view the demo on ncees.org/ExamPrep.

Examinee Guide

The *NCEES Examinee Guide* is the official guide to policies and procedures for all NCEES exams. During exam registration and again on exam day, examinees must agree to abide by the conditions in the *Examinee Guide*, which includes the CBT Examinee Rules and Agreement. You can download the *Examinee Guide* at ncees.org/exams. It is your responsibility to make sure you have the current version.

Scoring and reporting

Exam results for computer-based exams are typically available 7–10 days after you take the exam. You will receive an email notification from NCEES with instructions to view your results in your MyNCEES account. All results are reported as pass or fail.

Updates on exam content and procedures

Visit us at **ncees.org/exams** for updates on everything exam-related, including specifications, exam-day policies, scoring, and corrections to published exam preparation materials. This is also where you will register for the exam and find additional steps you should follow in your state to be approved for the exam.

EXAM SPECIFICATIONS

Fundamentals of Engineering (FE)
CHEMICAL CBT Exam Specifications
Effective Beginning with the July 2020 Examinations

- The FE exam is a computer-based test (CBT). It is closed book with an electronic reference.

- Examinees have 6 hours to complete the exam, which contains 110 questions. The 6-hour time also includes a tutorial and an optional scheduled break.

- The FE exam uses both the International System of Units (SI) and the U.S. Customary System (USCS).

Knowledge   **Number of Questions**

1. **Mathematics**   6–9
   A. Analytic geometry, logarithms, and trigonometry
   B. Calculus (e.g., single-variable, integral, differential)
   C. Differential equations (e.g., ordinary, partial, Laplace)
   D. Numerical methods (e.g., error propagation, Taylor's series, curve fitting, Newton-Raphson, Fourier series)
   E. Algebra (e.g., fundamentals, matrix algebra, systems of equations)
   F. Accuracy, precision, and significant figures

2. **Probability and Statistics**   4–6
   A. Probability distributions (e.g., discrete, continuous, normal, binomial)
   B. Expected value (weighted average) in decision making
   C. Hypothesis testing and design of experiments (e.g., t-test, outlier testing, analysis of the variance)
   D. Measures of central tendencies and dispersions (e.g., mean, mode, standard deviation, confidence intervals)
   E. Regression and curve fitting
   F. Statistical control (e.g., control limits)

3. **Engineering Sciences**   4–6
   A. Basic dynamics (e.g., friction, force, mass, acceleration, momentum)
   B. Work, energy, and power (as applied to particles or rigid bodies)
   C. Electricity, current, and voltage laws (e.g., charge, energy, current, voltage, power, Kirchhoff's law, Ohm's law)

4. **Materials Science**   4–6
   A. Chemical, electrical, mechanical, and physical properties (e.g., effect of temperature, pressure, stress, strain, failure)
   B. Material types and compatibilities (e.g., engineered materials, ferrous and nonferrous metals)
   C. Corrosion mechanisms and control
   D. Polymers, ceramics, and composites

5. **Chemistry and Biology**   7–11
    A. Inorganic chemistry (e.g., molarity, normality, molality, acids, bases, redox reactions, valence, solubility product, pH, pK, electrochemistry, periodic table)
    B. Organic chemistry (e.g., nomenclature, structure, balanced equations, reactions, synthesis)
    C. Analytical chemistry (e.g., wet chemistry and instrumental chemistry)
    D. Biochemistry, microbiology, and molecular biology (e.g., organization and function of the cell; Krebs, glycolysis, Calvin cycles; enzymes and protein chemistry; genetics; protein synthesis, translation, transcription)
    E. Bioprocessing (e.g., fermentation, biological treatment systems, aerobic, anaerobic process, nutrient removal)

6. **Fluid Mechanics/Dynamics**   8–12
    A. Fluid properties
    B. Dimensionless numbers (e.g., Reynolds number)
    C. Mechanical energy balance (e.g., pipes, valves, fittings, pressure losses across packed beds, pipe networks)
    D. Bernoulli equation (hydrostatic pressure, velocity head)
    E. Laminar and turbulent flow
    F. Flow measurement (e.g., orifices, Venturi meters)
    G. Pumps, turbines, compressors, and vacuum systems
    H. Compressible flow and non-Newtonian fluids

7. **Thermodynamics**   8–12
    A. Thermodynamic properties of pure components and mixtures (e.g., specific volume, internal energy, enthalpy, entropy, free energy, ideal gas law)
    B. Properties data and phase diagrams of pure components and mixtures (e.g., steam tables, psychrometric charts, T-s, P-h, x-y, T-x-y)
    C. Thermodynamic laws (e.g., first law, second law)
    D. Thermodynamic processes (e.g., isothermal, adiabatic, isentropic, phase changes)
    E. Cyclic processes and efficiencies (e.g., power, refrigeration, heat pump)
    F. Phase equilibrium (e.g., fugacity, activity coefficient, Raoult's law)
    G. Chemical equilibrium
    H. Heats of reaction and mixing

8. **Material/Energy Balances**   10–15
    A. Steady-state mass balance
    B. Unsteady-state mass balance
    C. Steady-state energy balance
    D. Unsteady-state energy balance
    E. Recycle/bypass processes
    F. Reactive systems (e.g., combustion)

9. **Heat Transfer**   8–12
   A. Conductive heat transfer
   B. Convective heat transfer (natural and forced)
   C. Radiation heat transfer
   D. Heat-transfer coefficients (e.g., overall, local, fouling)
   E. Heat-transfer equipment, operation, and design (e.g., double pipe, shell
      and tube, fouling, number of transfer units, log-mean temperature
      difference, flow configuration)

10. **Mass Transfer and Separation**   8–12
   A. Molecular diffusion (e.g., steady and unsteady state, physical property
      estimation)
   B. Convective mass transfer (e.g., mass-transfer coefficient, eddy diffusion)
   C. Separation systems (e.g., distillation, absorption, extraction, membrane
      processes, adsorption)
   D. Equilibrium stage methods (e.g., graphical methods, McCabe-Thiele,
      efficiency)
   E. Continuous contact methods (e.g., number of transfer units, height equivalent
      to a theoretical plate, height of transfer unit, number of theoretical plates)
   F. Humidification, drying, and evaporation

11. **Solids Handling**   3–5
   A. Particle properties (e.g., surface and bulk forces, particle size distribution)
   B. Processing (e.g., crushing, grinding, crystallization)
   C. Transportation and storage (e.g., belts, pneumatic, slurries, tanks, hoppers)

12. **Chemical Reaction Engineering**   7–11
   A. Reaction rates and order
   B. Rate constant (e.g., Arrhenius function)
   C. Conversion, yield, and selectivity
   D. Type of reactions (e.g., series, parallel, forward, reverse, homogeneous,
      heterogeneous, biological)
   E. Reactor types (e.g., batch, semibatch, continuous stirred tank, plug flow,
      gas phase, liquid phase)
   F. Catalysis (e.g., mechanisms, biocatalysis, physical properties)

13. **Economics**   4–6
   A. Time value of money (e.g., present worth, annual worth, future worth,
      rate of return)
   B. Economic analyses (e.g., break-even, benefit-cost, optimal economic life)
   C. Uncertainty (e.g., expected value and risk)
   D. Project selection (e.g., comparison of projects with unequal lives,
      lease/buy/make, depreciation, discounted cash flow)

14. **Process Design**   7–11
   A. Process flow diagrams and piping and instrumentation diagrams
   B. Equipment selection (e.g., sizing and scale-up)
   C. Equipment and facilities cost estimation (e.g., cost indices, equipment costing)
   D. Process design and optimization (e.g., sustainability, efficiency, green engineering, inherently safer design, evaluation of specifications, product design)
   E. Design standards (e.g., regulatory, ASTM, ISO, OSHA)

15. **Process Control**   4–6
   A. Dynamics (e.g., first- and second-order processes, gains and time constants, stability, damping, and transfer functions)
   B. Control strategies (e.g., feedback, feedforward, cascade, ratio, PID controller tuning, alarms, other safety equipment)
   C. Control loop design and hardware (e.g., matching measured and manipulated variables, sensors, control valves, conceptual process control, distributed control system [DCS] programming, programmable logic controller [PLC] programming, interlocks)

16. **Safety, Health, and Environment**   5–8
   A. Hazardous properties of materials, including SDS (e.g., corrosivity, flammability, toxicity, reactivity, handling, storage, transportation)
   B. Industrial hygiene (e.g., toxicity, noise, PPE, ergonomics)
   C. Process safety, risk assessment, and hazard analysis (e.g., layer of protection analysis, hazard and operability [HAZOP] studies, fault and event tree analysis, dispersion modeling)
   D. Overpressure and underpressure protection (e.g., relief, redundant control, inherently safe)
   E. Waste minimization, waste treatment, and regulation (e.g., air, water, solids, RCRA, CWA, other EPA, OSHA)
   F. Reactivity hazards (e.g., inerting, runaway reactions, compatibility)

17. **Ethics and Professional Practice**   3–5
   A. Codes of ethics (professional and technical societies)
   B. Agreements, contracts, and contract law (e.g., noncompete, nondisclosure, memorandum of understanding)
   C. Public health, safety, and welfare (e.g., public protection issues, licensing, professional liability, regulatory issues)
   D. Intellectual property (e.g., copyright, trade secrets, patents, trademarks)

FE CHEMICAL PRACTICE EXAM

1. Three lines are defined by the three equations:

$$x + y = 0$$
$$x - y = 0$$
$$2x + y = 1$$

The three lines form a triangle with vertices at:

- ○ A. $(0, 0), \left(\frac{1}{3}, \frac{1}{3}\right), (1, -1)$
- ○ B. $(0, 0), \left(\frac{2}{3}, \frac{2}{3}\right), (-1, -1)$
- ○ C. $(1, 1), (1, -1), (2, 1)$
- ○ D. $(1, 1), (3, -3), (-2, -1)$

2. Which of the following is the general solution to the differential equation and boundary condition shown below?

$$\frac{dy}{dt} + 5y = 0;\ y(0) = 1$$

- ○ A. e^{5t}
- ○ B. e^{-5t}
- ○ C. $e^{\sqrt{-5t}}$
- ○ D. $5e^{-5t}$

3. Suppose $f(t) = t^2$. The area under the curve for $0 \leq t \leq 2$, estimated by using the trapezoidal rule with $\Delta t = 0.5$, is most nearly:

- ○ A. 4.00
- ○ B. 2.75
- ○ C. 2.67
- ○ D. 1.33

4. A lab technician is preparing a chemical standard and has the following laboratory equipment and glassware.

Volumetric flask   100 ml ± 0.1 ml
Analytical balance   100 g ± 0.001 g
Glass pipette   1 ml ± 0.01 ml

The technician first weighs out 10 g of solids and dissolves them in 100 ml of water. Then the technician dilutes 1 ml of the solution to 100 ml using best laboratory practices. What is the number of significant figures of the molarity of the final solution?

- ○ A.   1
- ○ B.   2
- ○ C.   3
- ○ D.   4

5. Match the curve properties to the correct locations on the curve shown below.

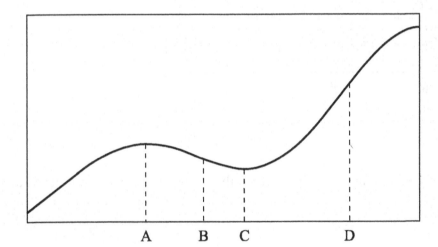

Points

A. ☐ ☐
B. ☐
C. ☐ ☐
D. ☐

Properties

$f' = 0$

$f'' = 0$

$f'' < 0$

$f'' > 0$

6. Plot the point on the log/log graph given below:

$X = 80,000$
$Y = 7,000$

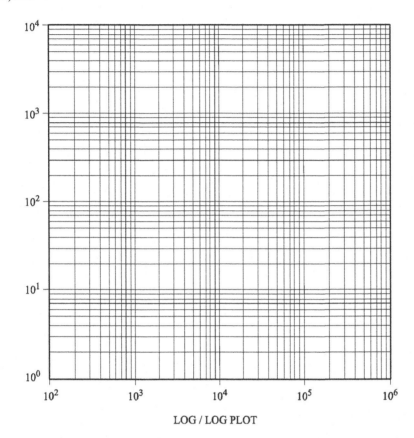

LOG / LOG PLOT

7. You have a fair coin that you toss ten times. The probability of getting exactly four heads in ten tosses is most nearly:

- ○ A.   0.1
- ○ B.   0.2
- ○ C.   0.4
- ○ D.   0.5

8. Suppose the lengths of telephone calls form a normal distribution with a mean length of 8.0 min and a standard deviation of 2.5 min. The probability that a telephone call selected at random will last more than 15.5 min is most nearly:

   ○ A. 0.0013
   ○ B. 0.0026
   ○ C. 0.2600
   ○ D. 0.9987

9. The standard deviation of the population of the three values 1, 4, and 7 is:

   ○ A. $\sqrt{3}$
   ○ B. $\sqrt{6}$
   ○ C. 4
   ○ D. 6

10. A ruggedized thermocouple used to measure process temperature has a time constant of 2.5 minutes. Considering the thermocouple as a first-order system with a gain of 1.00, the amount of time required to reach 99.9% of a new process temperature is most nearly:

   ○ A. 2.5 minutes
   ○ B. 5.0 minutes
   ○ C. 17.3 minutes
   ○ D. 3 weeks

11. A rod is shown in the figure below:

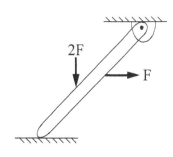

If the weight of the rod is neglected, which of the following is a correct free-body diagram?

Option A	**Option B**	**Option C**	**Option D**
		(see figure)	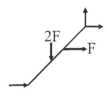

○ A. Option A
○ B. Option B
○ C. Option C
○ D. Option D

12. In the resistor circuit shown below, the equivalent resistance R_{eq} (Ω) at Terminals a-b is most nearly:

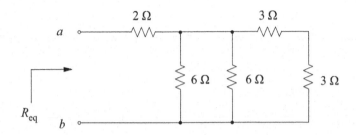

- A. 2
- B. 4
- C. 20
- D. 22

13. The value of the current i (amperes) in the network shown below is mostly nearly:

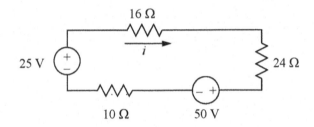

- A. 1.5
- B. 0.5
- C. −0.5
- D. −1.5

14. For the vector $\vec{r} = 12$ ft $\hat{\mathbf{i}} - 8$ ft $\hat{\mathbf{j}}$, select the graph that shows both the components and the resultant.

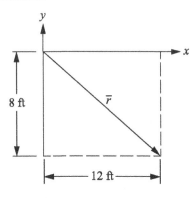

Option A

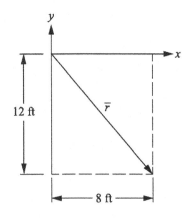

Option B

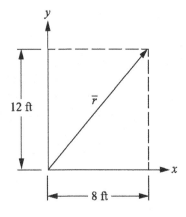

Option C

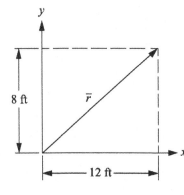

Option D

15.   A 0.25-m steel rod with a cross-sectional area of 1,250 mm² and a modulus of elasticity E of 200 GPa is subjected to a 5,000-N force as shown below. The elongation of the rod (μm) is most nearly:

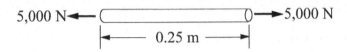

- ○ A.   2.4
- ○ B.   4.4
- ○ C.   5.0
- ○ D.   9.6

16.   In general, a metal with high hardness will also have which of the following characteristics?

Select **all** that apply.

- ☐ A.   Good formability
- ☐ B.   Strong intermolecular bonding
- ☐ C.   High tensile strength
- ☐ D.   High yield strength
- ☐ E.   High oxygen permeability
- ☐ F.   High abrasion/scratch resistance

17.   If an aluminum crimp connector were used to connect a copper wire to a battery, what would most likely happen?

- ○ A.   Only the copper wire will corrode.
- ○ B.   Only the aluminum connector will corrode.
- ○ C.   Both will corrode.
- ○ D.   Nothing

18. Glass is said to be an amorphous material. This means that it:

    ○ A. has a high melting point
    ○ B. is a supercooled vapor
    ○ C. has large cubic crystals
    ○ D. has no apparent crystal structure

19. Five columns—C1, C2, C3, C4, and C5—are labeled below in the Periodic Table of Elements. Select the columns that contain an element that could have either a +3 or –3 charge?

C1																	
I	C2											C4				C5	VIII
1 H 1.008	II											III	IV	V	VI	VII	He 4.0026
3 Li 6.94	4 Be 9.0122											5 B 10.81	6 C 12.011	7 N 14.007	8 O 15.999	9 F 18.998	10 Ne 20.180
11 Na 22.990	12 Mg 24.305					C3						13 Al 26.982	14 Si 28.085	15 P 30.974	16 S 32.06	17 Cl 35.45	18 Ar 39.948
19 K 39.098	20 Ca 40.078	21 Sc 44.956	22 Ti 47.867	23 V 50.942	24 Cr 51.996	25 Mn 54.938	26 Fe 55.845	27 Co 58.933	28 Ni 58.693	29 Cu 63.546	30 Zn 65.38	31 Ga 69.723	32 Ge 72.630	33 As 74.922	34 Se 78.971	35 Br 79.904	36 Kr 83.798
37 Rb 85.468	38 Sr 87.62	39 Y 88.906	40 Zr 91.224	41 Nb 92.906	42 Mo 95.95	43 Tc (98)	44 Ru 101.07	45 Rh 102.91	46 Pd 106.42	47 Ag 107.87	48 Cd 112.41	49 In 114.82	50 Sn 118.71	51 Sb 121.76	52 Te 127.60	53 I 126.90	54 Xe 131.29
55 Cs 132.91	56 Ba 137.33	57–71	72 Hf 178.49	73 Ta 180.95	74 W 183.84	75 Re 186.21	76 Os 190.23	77 Ir 192.22	78 Pt 195.08	79 Au 196.97	80 Hg 200.59	81 Tl 204.38	82 Pb 207.2	83 Bi 208.98	84 Po (209)	85 At (210)	86 Rn (222)
87 Fr (223)	88 Ra (226)	89–103	104 Rf (267)	105 Db (268)	106 Sg (269)	107 Bh (270)	108 Hs (277)	109 Mt (278)	110 Ds (281)	111 Rg (282)	112 Cn (285)	113 Nh (286)	114 Fl (289)	115 Mc (290)	116 Lv (293)	117 Ts (294)	118 Og (294)

Lanthanide Series	57 La 138.91	58 Ce 140.12	59 Pr 140.91	60 Nd 144.24	61 Pm (145)	62 Sm 150.36	63 Eu 151.96	64 Gd 157.25	65 Tb 158.93	66 Dy 162.50	67 Ho 164.93	68 Er 167.26	69 Tm 168.93	70 Yb 173.05	71 Lu 174.97
Actinide Series	89 Ac (227)	90 Th 232.04	91 Pa 231.04	92 U 238.03	93 Np (237)	94 Pu (244)	95 Am (243)	96 Cm (247)	97 Bk (247)	98 Cf (251)	99 Es (252)	100 Fm (257)	101 Md (258)	102 No (259)	103 Lr (266)

20. In the double replacement reaction between silver nitrate and hydrochloric acid, which one of the following would be a reaction product?

   ○ A.   Chlorine gas
   ○ B.   Nitrous oxide
   ○ C.   Silver chloride
   ○ D.   Silver hypochlorite

21. How is a solution with a pH of 2 prepared using 6 M HCl?

   ○ A.   Dilute 1.67 mL of HCl to 1 L, using water.

   ○ B.   Dilute 6 mL of HCl to 1 L, using water.

   ○ C.   Dilute 16.7 mL of HCl to 1 L, using water.

   ○ D.   Dilute 60 mL of HCl to 1 L, using water.

22. The number of hydrogen atoms in a molecule of dodecane is:

   ○ A.   6
   ○ B.   12
   ○ C.   20
   ○ D.   26

23. Which analytical equipment provides the best method to analyze the Hg concentration to parts per million in a groundwater sample?

   ○ A.   Gas chromatograph
   ○ B.   Viscometer
   ○ C.   Atomic adsorption unit
   ○ D.   X-ray diffraction unit

24. The balanced equation and molecular weights for reactants and products in the anaerobic digestion of an organic material are as follows:

$$C_{60}H_{94}O_{38}N + 18\ H_2O \rightarrow 32\ CH_4 + 28\ CO_2 + NH_3$$

Compound	MW
$C_{60}H_{94}O_{38}N$	1,433
H_2O	18
CH_4	16
CO_2	44
NH_3	17

The weight (lb) of methane produced per 2,000 lb of organic material would be most nearly_____.

25. In the production of wine using yeast, grape juice is fermented in special tanks equipped with pressure relief valves. These valves are used to prevent overpressurization from which one of the following yeast reactions?

- ○ A.   The yeast produces oxygen gas from aerobic respiration.
- ○ B.   The yeast produces oxygen gas from anaerobic respiration.
- ○ C.   The yeast produces carbon dioxide during fermentation.
- ○ D.   The yeast could produce both carbon dioxide and oxygen during the fermentation process.

26. Water is warmed from 5°C to 25°C. The specific gravity of the water will:

- ○ A.   decrease to 0.997
- ○ B.   increase to 1.003
- ○ C.   increase to 1.017
- ○ D.   not change at all

27. Water at 10°C is flowing at a velocity of 0.52 m/s through pipe with an inside diameter of 1.25 cm. The flow through the pipe can be described as:

   ○ A.   laminar
   ○ B.   transitional between laminar and turbulent
   ○ C.   turbulent
   ○ D.   Water flow at 0.52 m/s through a 1.25-cm pipe is not possible

28. Water is discharged to the atmosphere as a jet from a puncture in the bottom of a ventilated storage tank. The storage tank is a cylinder 6 m high, mounted on a level platform 2 m off the ground. Neglecting losses, the jet velocity (m/s) when the tank is half full is most nearly:

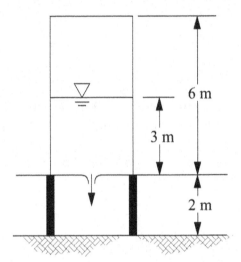

   ○ A.   7.7
   ○ B.   9.9
   ○ C.   12.5
   ○ D.   50.8

29. The fluid property most related to a fluid flow characteristics is:

- ○ A. thermal conductivity
- ○ B. mass diffusivity
- ○ C. heat capacity
- ○ D. viscosity

30. A 200-mm-diameter pipe is flowing full in laminar flow with a centerline velocity of 10 m/s. The velocity (m/s) at a point 80 mm from the centerline is most nearly:

- ○ A. 1.0
- ○ B. 2.0
- ○ C. 3.6
- ○ D. 8.4

31. The pitot tube shown below is placed at a point where the velocity is 2.0 m/s. The specific gravity of the fluid is 2.0, and the upper portion of the manometer contains air. The reading h (m) on the manometer is most nearly:

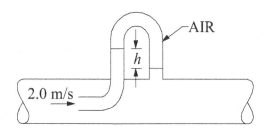

- ○ A. 20.0
- ○ B. 10.0
- ○ C. 0.40
- ○ D. 0.20

32. Two identical centrifugal pumps are pumping into a line taking waste to a treatment system. The pumps are operating at the same speed and are arranged in parallel and taking suction from the same constant-level wastewater sump.

The pump curve for each pump is shown below. Another curve showing the head loss in the wastewater line versus flow rate is also shown. Select the shaded point on the pump curve that indicates the head and flow for each pump.

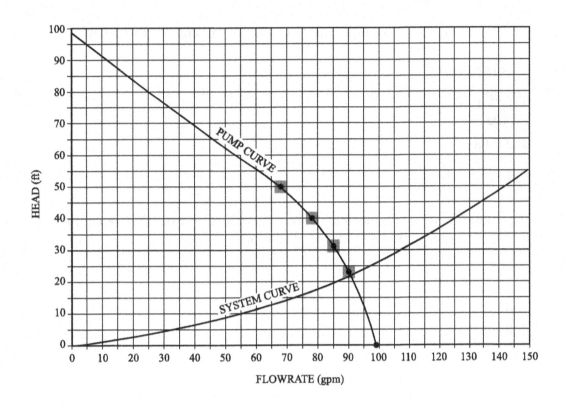

33.	Air from a 100-psig source is free-flowing down a long pipe discharging to the atmosphere. This is an example of what kind of fluid flow?

○ A.	Incompressible
○ B.	Inviscous
○ C.	Compressible
○ D.	Viscous

34.	The pressure of 100 kg of nitrogen (N_2) at 70°C in a 100-m³ tank is most nearly:

○ A.	2,850 kPa
○ B.	102 kPa
○ C.	20 kPa
○ D.	102 mPa

35.	HFC-134a enters an evaporator at a quality of 0.1 and 20°C. It exits the evaporator as a saturated vapor at 20°C. The energy (kJ/kg) added is most nearly:

○ A.	170
○ B.	250
○ C.	300
○ D.	420

36. For each binary phase diagram below, indicate whether or not the system exhibits an azeotrope.

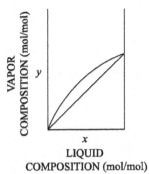

Option A _____

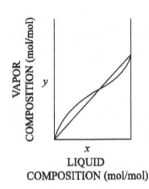

Option B _____

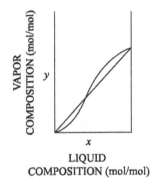

Option C _____

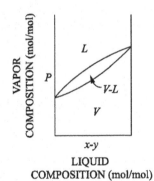

Option D _____

NO AZEOTROPE

AZEOTROPE

37. The work (kJ) required to compress 1,000 L of an ideal gas to 500 L at a constant pressure of 100 kPa in a closed system is most nearly:

- ○ A.   0.2
- ○ B.   5
- ○ C.   50
- ○ D.   600

38. A mixture of alcohols is fed to a process. The molar composition of the mixture and the individual vapor pressures for the pure components are shown in the table:

Alcohol	Molar Composition in Mixture (%)	Vapor Pressure (kPa)
Methanol	12	16.9
Ethanol	34	12.4
Propanol	22	2.8
1-Butanol	32	0.93

Assume the alcohols form an ideal liquid solution in which Raoult's law applies. The pressure (kPa) at which the mixture is a bubble point liquid is most nearly:

- ○ A.   0.93
- ○ B.   7.2
- ○ C.   7.6
- ○ D.   33

39. Which of the following statements about flow through an insulated valve is most accurate?

- ○ A.   The enthalpy rises.
- ○ B.   The upstream and downstream enthalpies are equal.
- ○ C.   Temperature increases sharply.
- ○ D.   Pressure increases sharply.

40. The ratio of partial pressure to the saturation pressure of water at a given temperature is:

- ○ A. specific humidity
- ○ B. relative humidity
- ○ C. dew-point temperature
- ○ D. wet-bulb temperature

41. The Ag-Cu binary phase diagram is shown below.

Mark the eutectic point on the diagram.

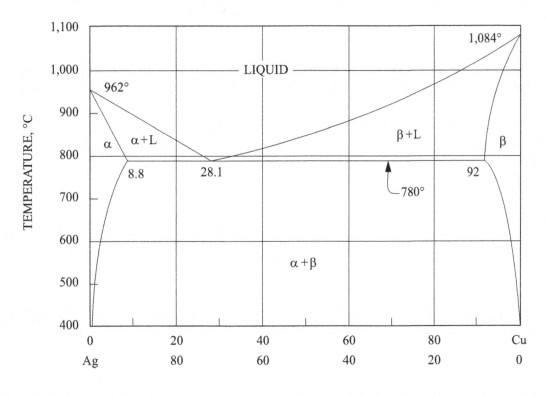

COMPOSITION, % BY WEIGHT

42. Pure CO_2 can be prepared by treating a dry mixture of $MgCO_3$, $CaCO_3$, and inerts with a sulfuric acid solution. In a batch reactor, the reaction material is heated, some of the water is evaporated, and some CO_2 is removed. The residue slurry in the reactor has the following composition:

Component	Weight Percent
Water	85.00
$CaSO_4$	8.30
$MgSO_4$	5.00
H_2SO_4	1.00
Inert	0.60
CO_2	0.10

Molecular Weights	
H_2O	18.02
H_2SO_4	98.08
CO_2	44.01
$CaSO_4$	136.15
$MgSO_4$	120.38
$MgCO_3$	84.32
$CaCO_3$	100.09

$$CaCO_3 + H_2SO_4 \rightarrow CaSO_4 + CO_2 + H_2O$$
$$MgCO_3 + H_2SO_4 \rightarrow MgSO_4 + CO_2 + H_2O$$

The mass (kg) of dry mixture fed (including inerts) per 100 kg of residue is most nearly:

- A. 13.9
- B. 13.3
- C. 10.2
- D. 9.6

43.   A plant that concentrates an aqueous solution of sodium hydroxide uses a forward-feed, triple-effect evaporator as shown below. The operating parameters are shown on the figure. Sodium hydroxide concentrations are given in wt%. The flow of vapor from Effect III (kg/hr) is most nearly:

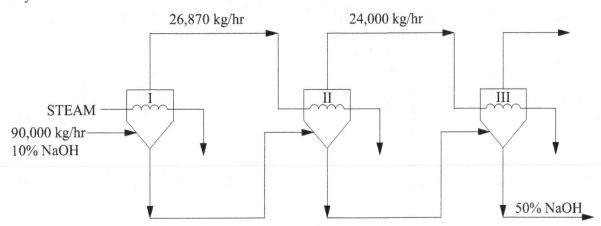

- O   A.   72,000
- O   B.   57,000
- O   C.   30,000
- O   D.   21,000

44.   An insulated, steam-heated, single-stage laboratory evaporator is used to determine data for the design of large units. Saturated steam at 150°C is used as the heating medium. The steam condensate is all liquid at 150°C. The total heat duty is 225 kW. The required steam rate (kg/s) is most nearly:

- O   A.   9.40
- O   B.   8.56
- O   C.   0.11
- O   D.   0.08

45. In this distillation column, Feed F contains Components A, B, and C. If $x_{B,F}$ is the mole fraction of Component B in Feed F, then the overall material balance of Component B in this column is:

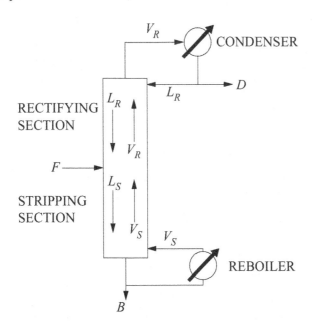

- A. $F = L_R + L_S - V_R - V_S$

- B. $L_R x_{B,L_R} + V_R x_{B,V_R} = L_S x_{B,L_S} + V_S x_{B,V_S}$

- C. $V x_{B,D} = V_R x_{B,V_R} + L_R x_{B,L_R}$

- D. $F x_{B,F} = D x_{B,D} + B x_{B,B}$

46. A batch of liquid is to be heated by a submerged steam coil in a closed vessel. Heat losses to the surroundings can be neglected. The following data apply:

Mass of liquid, m	1,000 kg
Liquid temperature, T	K
Initial liquid temperature, T_o	K
Steam temperature, T_s	390 K
Liquid heat capacity, c	3.8 kJ/(kg·K)
Surface area of heating coil, A	1.0 m^2
Overall heat-transfer coefficient, U	600 W/(m^2·K)
Time, t	s

The equation that describes the batch heating time is:

    A. $mc\dfrac{dT}{dt} + UAT_o = UAT$

    B. $mc\dfrac{dT}{dt} = UA(T_s - T)$

    C. $t = \dfrac{UA}{mc}(T - T_o)$

    D. $\exp\left(\dfrac{T_s - T_o}{T_s - T}\right) = \dfrac{UA}{mc}t$

47. The feed to a plant producing methanol consists of hydrogen and carbon monoxide in a ratio of 2.050 moles of H_2 per mole of CO. The feed rate to the plant is 1,230 kmol/hr. The single-pass conversion of the carbon monoxide in the reactor is 35%. The feed to the reactor (M) has a H_2/CO molar ratio of 2.250/1.000. A purge stream (W) is provided to maintain this ratio.

A separation system, as shown in the figure, is provided to recover pure methanol from the reactor effluent. The methanol recovery is 100%. The composition of the recycle stream (R) is 70.45% H_2 and 29.55% CO. The overall conversion of CO is most nearly:

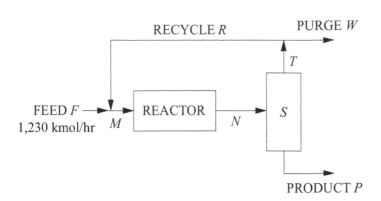

- ○ A.   35%
- ○ B.   42%
- ○ C.   70%
- ○ D.   87%

48. It is desired to burn liquid propane, C_3H_8, with excess air, both supplied at 25°C. Assume that air is 21 vol% oxygen, and the balance is nitrogen. If 1.00 mol of propane is burned with x mols of air, how many mols of oxygen appear in the combustion products?

- ○ A. $3.0 + 0.21x$
- ○ B. $4.0 + 0.79x$
- ○ C. $0.79x$
- ○ D. $0.21x - 5.0$

49. A low-energy gas is burned in a furnace with excess air. The feed rate is 2,500 m³/hr of gas at 0°C and 1 atm.

Low-Energy Gas		
Compound	Mol%	MW
CO	16.0	28
CO₂	12.6	44
H₂	19.0	2
CH₄	52.4	16

Flue Gas (Dry Basis)		
Compound	Mol%	MW
CO₂	13.5	44
N₂	84.4	28
O₂	2.1	32

The amount (kmol) of air supplied per 100 kmol of dry flue gas is most nearly:

- A. 10
- B. 17
- C. 110
- D. 400

50. A 19 wt% NaOH solution is made by diluting 500 kg/hr of 50% NaOH with the appropriate amount of water. The heat of dilution causes the resulting 19 wt% NaOH to warm to 50°C. The heat capacity, c_p, of the 19 wt% NaOH solution is 3.77 kJ/(kg·°C). The rate (kJ/hr) at which heat must be removed from this solution to cool it to 30°C is most nearly:

- A. 7,200
- B. 38,000
- C. 94,000
- D. 99,000

51. Seventy-five tons per hour (tph) of calcium carbonate with 9.3% moisture is to be dried in a rotary dryer. Thirty percent of the feed exiting the dryer is recycled back to the beginning of the process and joins the incoming moist feed into the dryer. If 68.5 tph of product is produced, the percent moisture of the dried product exiting the dryer is most nearly:

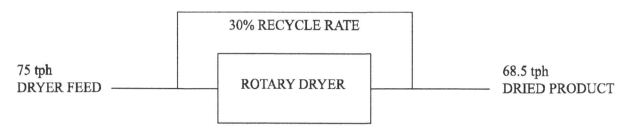

- O A.　　No moisture, it is completely dry
- O B.　　0.70 %
- O C.　　3.1 %
- O D.　　7.1 %

52. A large pipe carries steam. The outside pipe surface is at 200°C. For personnel safety, the pipe is insulated so that the temperature of the external surface insulation is less than 45°C. Neglect pipe curvature. The following data apply:

   Thermal conductivity of insulation = 0.035 W/(m·K)
   Combined radiation and convection coefficient for insulated pipe = 12 W/(m²·K)
   Surroundings and air temperature = 30°C

   The thickness (mm) of insulation is most nearly:

   ○ A.   3
   ○ B.   11
   ○ C.   15
   ○ D.   30

53. A nuclear reactor fuel tank consists of a metallic uranium cylinder 1.905 cm in diameter with an aluminum cladding 0.127 cm thick. The fuel element is placed axially in a channel 3.81 cm in diameter. The coolant is water that enters at 80°C at a flow rate of 130 L/min. The heat flux at a given point in the reactor is constant at 3.4×10^6 W/m² measured at the surface of the aluminum cladding.

   If the flow rate of the cooling water is doubled, the ratio of the new to the old heat-transfer coefficient is most nearly:

   ○ A.   0.5
   ○ B.   0.6
   ○ C.   1.7
   ○ D.   2.0

FE CHEMICAL PRACTICE EXAM

54. Waste heat is to be recovered from a 1.0 L/s condensate stream using a newly installed counter-current heat exchanger. The exchanger is a shell-and-tube exchanger with a single tube pass. The condensate is to be cooled from 60°C to 30°C. A 10% potassium nitrate solution is to be heated in the exchanger from 15°C to 35°C. During initial operation, the following data were collected:

Condensate
  Heat capacity = 4.2 J/(g·K)
  Density = 1.0 g/cm^3

KNO_3 stream
  Heat capacity = 5.0 J/(g·K)
  Density = 1.2 g/cm^3

Tubing
  I.D. = 0.012 m
  O.D. = 0.015 m
  Tube length = 1.8 m
  Number of tubes = 54
  Thermal conductivity = 380 W/(m·K)

Individual heat-transfer coefficients
  Tube-side coefficient = 8,700 W/(m^2·K)
  Shell-side coefficient = 1,750 W/(m^2·K)

The overall shell-side heat-transfer coefficient [W/(m^2·K)] is most nearly:

- ○ A. 1,400
- ○ B. 1,750
- ○ C. 8,700
- ○ D. 14,000

Copyright © 2020 by NCEES   36   NEXT→

55. A 50-cm-diameter steel ball is radiating heat to its surroundings at a rate of 73 W with a surface temperature of 75°C. The following information about the steel is known. If ambient temperature is 22°C, what type of steel is the ball most likely constructed of?

Steel type	Emissivity, ε
Galvanized	0.23
Mild	0.32
Stainless, Type 301	0.59
Oxidized	0.79

- ○ A. Galvanized
- ○ B. Mild
- ○ C. Stainless
- ○ D. Oxidized

56. The overall heat-transfer coefficient U for a heat exchanger has units of energy per time per area per temperature degrees. The inverse of the overall heat-transfer coefficient is known as the heat-transfer resistance R. Which of the following are suitable units for R?

- ○ A. $cm^3/kW \cdot °C$
- ○ B. $sec \cdot m^2 \cdot K/kW$
- ○ C. $W/sec \cdot m^2 \cdot K$
- ○ D. $ft^2 \cdot °R \cdot min/Btu$

57.   A double-pipe heat exchanger is used to heat air. The air enters at 10°C and is heated to 90°C. For air, $C_p = 1.007$ kJ/(kg·K). For an airflow rate of 7,500 kg/min, the heat-transfer rate (W) to the air is most nearly:

○ A. 1.01×10^7
○ B. 7.75×10^6
○ C. 1.01×10^6
○ D. 7.75×10^5

58.   Certain compact heat exchangers have small rectangular channels through which one or more heat-transfer media flow. It is necessary to know the hydraulic diameter of the channels to calculate Reynolds numbers, Nusselt numbers, and heat-transfer coefficients for these configurations. For a given geometry, the hydraulic diameter is computed as four times the cross-sectional area of the channel divided by its wetted perimeter. Therefore, such a rectangular channel with a width of 10 mm and a height of 4 mm has a hydraulic diameter (mm) of most nearly:

○ A.   5.7
○ B.   7.0
○ C.   10.8
○ D.   11.4

59. Match the heat exchanger temperature profile below with the correct type.

TEMPERATURE PROFILES

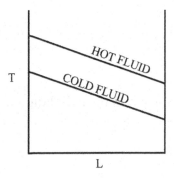

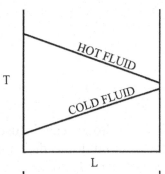

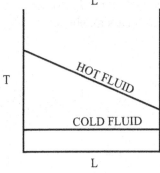

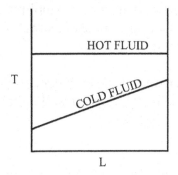

COCURRENT FLOW,
NO PHASE CHANGE

CONDENSATION

COUNTERCURRENT FLOW,
NO PHASE CHANGE

EVAPORATION

60. A liquid is flowing inside a tube coated with a slightly soluble inorganic salt having a molecular weight of 250. The inside diameter of the coated tube is 5.0 cm. The following data apply:

Reynolds number = 30,000
Schmidt number = 6.0
Diffusion coefficient of the salt in the liquid = 1.0×10^{-5} cm^2/s
Solubility of the salt in the liquid = 2.0×10^{-4} mol/cm^3

After the boundary layer is established but before there is significant salt in the bulk liquid, the flux [mol/(s·m^2)] of the salt into the flowing liquid is most nearly:

- A. 6.38×10^{-4}
- B. 2.39×10^{-3}
- C. 3.89×10^{-3}
- D. 6.11×10^{-3}

61. Gaseous hydrogen is contained in a steel cylinder at 15 bars and 27°C. Hydrogen can diffuse into bubble defects in the cylinder wall, causing embrittlement and consequent failure. A defect is located 2 mm from the inner surface of the cylinder. The cylinder can be considered large enough that the radial effects can be neglected. The system then transforms as shown:

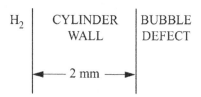

The molar concentration of the hydrogen at the inner surface of the cylinder is 1.50 kmol/m^3 and is initially zero at the surface of the defect. The initial pressure of inert gas in the defect is 1.0 bar. The diffusion coefficient of hydrogen in steel is 0.3×10^{-12} m^2/s.

If a linear concentration profile were established between the inner wall of the cylinder and the innermost edge of the defect before the concentration in the defect changed significantly, the molar flux [kmol/(m^2·s)] of the hydrogen into the defect would be most nearly:

- A. 1.13×10^{-10}
- B. 1.50×10^{-10}
- C. 2.25×10^{-10}
- D. 4.50×10^{-13}

62. The dimensionless Sherwood number, sometimes known as the mass transfer Nusselt number, represents the ratio of convective to diffusive mass transfer.

    Match the variables below with the relationship required to determine the Sherwood number.

$$Sh = \frac{[\underline{\hspace{2cm}}] \times [\underline{\hspace{2cm}}]}{[\underline{\hspace{2cm}}]}$$

Variables

Diffusion Coefficient   Pipe Inner Diameter   Overhead Product Rate

Mass-Transfer Coefficient   Molar-Flux Coefficient   Universal Gas Constant

63. The following figure is the solution of a binary distillation tower design using the McCabe-Thiele method. The equilibrium curve shown is for Component A. Component A is separated from B in the distillation column to produce a distillate that is 97 mole% A. The feed rate to the tower is 100 kmol/hr. The tower includes a partial reboiler and total condenser. The total number of ideal stages is:

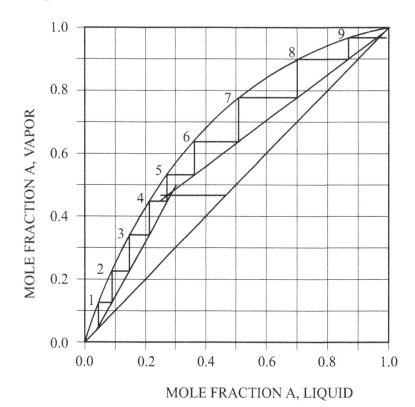

- ○ A.   7 in the column, plus reboiler and condenser
- ○ B.   8 in the column, plus condenser
- ○ C.   8 in the column, plus reboiler
- ○ D.   9 in the column

64. The following figure is the solution of a binary distillation tower design using the McCabe-Thiele method. The equilibrium curve shown is for Component A. Component A is separated from B in the distillation column to produce a distillate that is 97 mole% A. The feed rate to the tower is 100 kmol/hr. The tower includes a partial reboiler and total condenser. The bottoms flow rate (kmol/hr) is most nearly:

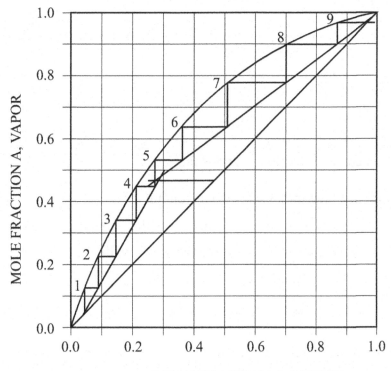

- ○ A. 3.0
- ○ B. 42.6
- ○ C. 53.8
- ○ D. 97.0

65. The following data apply to a mixture of copper and silver at 500°C:

$D_o = 1.9 \times 10^{-5} \text{ m}^2/\text{s}$
$Q_d = 150{,}000 \text{ J/mole}$

The diffusion coefficient (m^2/s) of the mixture is most nearly:

- A. 2.1×10^{-16}
- B. 1.4×10^{-15}
- C. 7.2×10^{-11}
- D. 5.7×10^{-7}

66. In a continuous distillation column, the reflux ratio is the:

- A. fraction of the total distillate that is returned to column
- B. ratio of the distillate returned to the column to the distillate removed as product
- C. ratio of the distillate returned to the column to the total distillate
- D. ratio of the vapor rate to the liquid rate within the column

67. Saturated moist air containing 1.2 kg of water to 50 kg of dry air produces an air-water mixture with a temperature of most nearly:

- A. 17°C
- B. 28°C
- C. 47°C
- D. 89°C

68. A wastewater treatment plant pumps a sludge slurry from the plant at a rate of 55 tph at 38% solids. The sludge goes through an inclined screw conveyor that removes 67% of the moisture followed by a belt filter press which removes 89% of the remaining moisture as it exits the screw conveyor. The low-moisture sludge then drops into a storage bunker to be transported to the local landfill. The final moisture content of the sludge in the storage bunker is most nearly:

- A. 12.5%
- B. 11.0%
- C. 5.6%
- D. 2.0%

69. The equipment least likely to be used to make a gas/solid separation is a(an):

   ○ A.   electrostatic precipitator
   ○ B.   centrifuge
   ○ C.   cyclone
   ○ D.   baghouse

70. The angle of repose for various materials in perfect cone-shaped piles is shown below.

Material	Angle of Repose (degrees)
Fine salt	25
Dry sand	34
Crushed gravel	40
Wood chips	45
Urea fertilizer	27

   Which of the following materials will have a cone taller than 14 ft if the material pile base has a diameter of 48 ft?

   ☐ A.   Fine salt
   ☐ B.   Dry sand
   ☐ C.   Crushed gravel
   ☐ D.   Wood chips
   ☐ E.   Urea fertilizer

71. A liquid-phase reaction $A \rightarrow B + C$ is second order in A with a rate constant of 0.01 L/(mol·s) at 100°C. The initial concentration of A in the feed mixture is 25 mol/L. If the reaction is carried out in a batch reactor and the conversion of A is 80%, then the time (min) required for this reaction at 100°C is most nearly:

   ○ A.   100
   ○ B.   16
   ○ C.   1.7
   ○ D.   0.27

72. Kinetic experiments were performed in a batch reactor based on the reversible first-order reaction A$\rightleftarrows$R. When $C_{R_0}/C_{A_0} = 1.6$, the equilibrium conversion is 92% at 25°C. If the conversion is 60% after 4 hr, the forward reaction rate constant (min^{-1}) is most nearly:

- ○ A. 0.0042
- ○ B. 0.021
- ○ C. 0.42
- ○ D. 0.21

73. The rate equation $-r_A = k_1 C_A - k_2 C_B$ describes a:

- ○ A. series reaction
- ○ B. parallel reaction
- ○ C. first-order reversible reaction
- ○ D. first-order irreversible reaction

74. A study of a liquid-phase reaction is performed to determine the effect of temperature on the reaction rate constant.

At 40°C, $k = 0.5$ sec^{-1}
At 70°C, $k = 1.1$ sec^{-1}

At 100°C, k (sec^{-1}) is most nearly:

- ○ A. 1.3
- ○ B. 1.5
- ○ C. 2.1
- ○ D. 2.8

75. The oxidation of an organic compound, A, produces two products, B and C, by competing reactions:

$$A + O_2 \rightarrow B$$
$$A + O_2 \rightarrow C + D$$

If the conversion of A is 80% and the selectivity of Species B to C is 9.0, the number of moles of B formed per mole of A fed to the oxidation reactor is most nearly:

- A. 0.08
- B. 0.40
- C. 0.72
- D. 0.90

76. Operating conditions for a plug-flow reactor for the elementary liquid-phase reaction $A + B \rightarrow R$ are as follows:

$$C_{A0} = 0.10 \text{ kmol/m}^3$$
$$C_{B0} = 0.10 \text{ kmol/m}^3$$
$$V = 0.50 \text{ m}^3$$
$$q = 0.20 \text{ m}^3/\text{min}$$
$$C_A \text{ (at exit)} = 0.040 \text{ kmol/m}^3$$

The space time (min) for this reactor is most nearly:

- A. 0.25
- B. 0.40
- C. 2.0
- D. 2.5

77. Compound A is a catalyst for a chemical reaction. Which of the following describes Compound A?

- A. Compound A is recoverable at the end of the reaction.
- B. Compound A is used up as part of the reaction.
- C. Compound A permanently bonds to one of the reactants.
- D. Compound A prevents the reaction.

78. The costs associated with building a chemical plant are shown below:

Cost of land = $10,000
Total fixed capital investment = $150,000
Fixed capital investment during Year 1 = $90,000
Fixed capital investment during Year 2 = $60,000
Plant start-up at the end of Year 2 = ?
Working capital = $30,000 at end of Year 2

In the cumulative cashflow diagram shown, select the area of the graph which best represents the capital investment during Year 2 of the process.

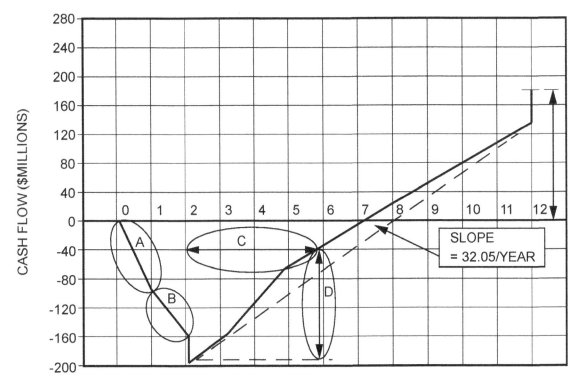

79. If $500 is invested at an annual interest rate of 8% per year, its future worth at the end of 30 years will be most nearly:

○ A. $1,200

○ B. $1,700

○ C. $5,031

○ D. $15,000

80. A control estimate was developed for a project based on a 30% level of project definition. To increase the level of project definition and produce a check estimate, the minimum level of project definition needed is most nearly:

   - A. 30%
   - B. 40%
   - C. 50%
   - D. 60%

81. A company can manufacture a product using hand tools. Tools will cost $1,000, and the manufacturing cost per unit will be $1.50. As an alternative, an automated system will cost $15,000 with a manufacturing cost per unit of $0.50. With an anticipated annual volume of 5,000 units and neglecting interest, the payback period (yr) is most nearly:

   - A. 2.8
   - B. 3.6
   - C. 15.0
   - D. never

82. A piping and instrumentation diagram (P&ID) would **not** contain which of the following?

   - A. Insulation specification identification
   - B. Process stream compositions
   - C. Fail/close or fail/open indication for valves
   - D. Locations of safety interlocks

83. Which of the following situations is most appropriate for using breakeven analysis?

   - A. Calculating the interest rate that will ensure that costs and returns are equal
   - B. Determining the number of units to produce to ensure that income covers expenses
   - C. Establishing the minimum return on an investment over a set number of years
   - D. Forecasting the amount of product that must be produced to meet a set profit margin

84. Using the pump curve shown below, you need to specify a pump to deliver 22 m³/hr at a head of 15 m. Match the impeller diameter, the pump horsepower, and the pump efficiency with the most appropriate measurement.

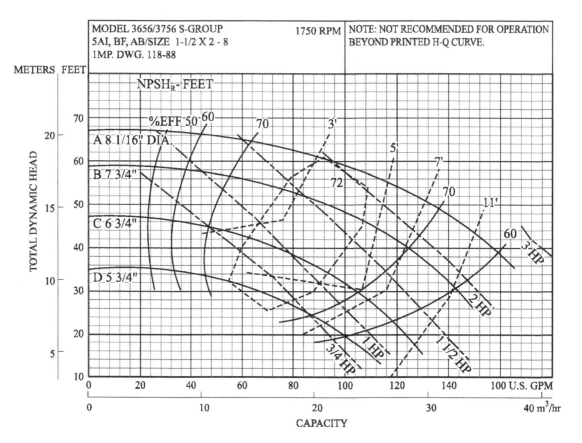

Pump Characteristics	Value
Impeller diameter (in.)	1 1/2
Pump horsepower (hp)	2
	7 3/4
Pump efficiency (%)	8 1/6
	6 3/4
	70
	72
	99

85. A recently purchased shell-and-tube, floating head, carbon steel heat exchanger containing 400 ft^2 of surface area cost $8,700. The estimated purchase cost of a similar exchanger containing 200 ft^2 of surface area is most nearly:

   ○ A. $4,350

   ○ B. $5,740

   ○ C. $6,410

   ○ D. $13,200

86. The recognized standard for pressure vessel design is published and maintained by which organization?

   ○ A. American Society of Mechanical Engineers (ASME)

   ○ B. Institute of Electrical and Electronics Engineers (IEEE)

   ○ C. Environmental Protection Agency (EPA)

   ○ D. National Fire Protection Association (NFPA)

87. The following table is a summation of manufacturing and product sales profits from a 5-year period. Also shown is a graph of the % sales profit per unit, the manufacturing cost per unit, and the pounds of waste generated per unit. Select the area on the table that shows where the plant's profitability is maximized.

PRODUCTION VOLUME (UNITS/DAY)	MANUFACTURING COST ($/UNIT)	SALES PROFIT (%/UNIT)	OVERALL PROFIT ($/DAY)	WASTE GENERATED (LB/UNIT)
100	15	83	7,200	32
150	12	86	11,250	34
200	16	82	14,200	38
250	17	80	17,500	40
300	18	79	20,700	46
350	22	75	22,750	58
400	28	68	23,600	62
450	38	56	22,050	69
500	50	43	18,500	71
550	65	25	12,100	73
600	75	14	7,200	76

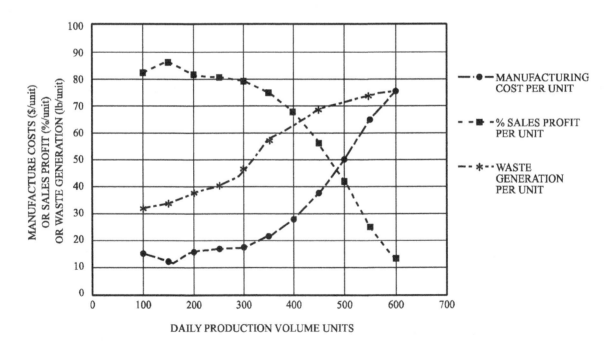

88. You must choose between four pieces of comparable equipment based on the cash flows given below. All four pieces have a life of 8 years.

Parameter	Equipment			
	A	B	C	D
First cost	$25,000	$35,000	$20,000	$40,000
Annual costs	$8,000	$6,000	$9,000	$5,000
Salvage value	$2,500	$3,500	$2,000	$4,000

The discount rate is 12%. Ignore taxes. The two most preferable pieces of equipment and the difference between their present worth values are most nearly:

- ○ A. A and C, $170
- ○ B. B and D, $170
- ○ C. A and C, $234
- ○ D. B and D, $234

89. A feedback control system is represented by the following figure.

$$G_P(s) = \frac{0.1}{(s + 1)(2s + 1)}$$

Which statement correctly describes the stability of the system?

- ○ A. The system is stable for $K_C > 0$.
- ○ B. The system is unstable for $K_C > 10$.
- ○ C. The system is stable only if K_C is in the range $0 < K_C < 22$.
- ○ D. The system is stable only if K_C is in the range $0 < K_C < 8$.

90.   The control strategy shown below is a good example of:

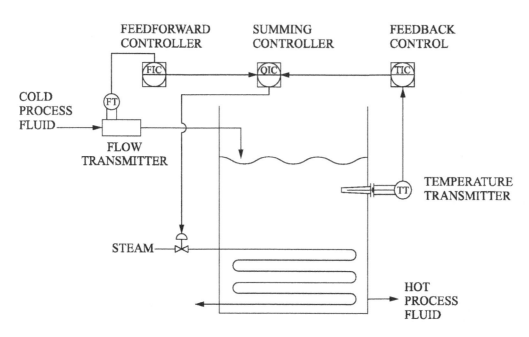

- ○ A.   feedforward control
- ○ B.   feedback and feedforward control
- ○ C.   feedback control
- ○ D.   damping control

91.   The closed-loop transfer function $C(s)/R(s)$ of the block diagram is:

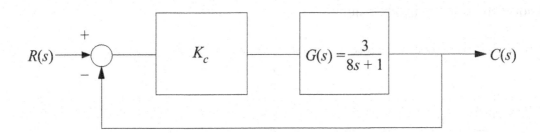

- ○ A. $\dfrac{3}{8s + K_c}$

- ○ B. $\dfrac{3K_c}{8s + K_c}$

- ○ C. $\dfrac{3}{8s + K_c - 1}$

- ○ D. $\dfrac{3K_c}{8s + 1 + 3K_c}$

92.   The figure below shows a block diagram for a process control system.

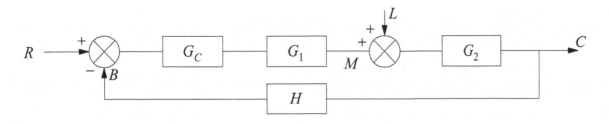

The closed-loop transfer function C/R is:

- ○ A. $\dfrac{G_2 G_1 G_C}{1 + G_2 G_1 G_C H}$

- ○ B. $\dfrac{G_2 G_1 G_C}{1 - G_2 G_1 G_C H}$

- ○ C. $G_2 G_1 G_C$

- ○ D. $G_2 G_1 G_C H$

93.   Long-term exposure to loud noises is known to cause hearing loss. OSHA has limits on the number of hours allowed at a specified noise level. For the noise environment specified below, is a noise abatement program required?

Noise Level (dBa)	Time Exposed (hr)
80	16
90	4
100	1

○ A.   No, a noise abatement program is not required.

○ B.   The question does not include sufficient information to determine if a program is needed.

○ C.   Yes, a noise abatement program is required.

○ D.   The answer depends on the results of a hearing conservation program.

94.   A Safety Data Sheet (SDS) provides information about chemicals and is essential for conducting a hazard analysis. Which information below can be obtained from an SDS?

Select **all** that apply.

☐ A.   Indication of whether a chemical is flammable or toxic

☐ B.   Recommendations for fire extinguishers that are compatible with the chemical

☐ C.   Permissible exposure limits (PELs) for the chemical

☐ D.   Recommendations for materials of construction to be used with the chemical

☐ E.   Physical properties of the chemical

☐ F.   Reactions for producing the chemical

☐ G.   Recommendations for personal protective equipment to be used with the chemical

95.   A chemical storage tank is steam-cleaned with superheated steam. Immediately after steaming, the tank is sealed and left to cool overnight. The significant consequence of this would most likely be that the:

    ○ A.   condensed steam may contain corrosive contaminants that damage the tank

    ○ B.   reduced pressure within the tank could cause the tank to collapse

    ○ C.   tank would not cool as fast as if it were vented

    ○ D.   maximum design temperature would be exceeded

96.   A total of 50 g of dry-cleaning fluid (perchloroethylene) is spilled and allowed to evaporate in a 4-m × 4-m × 4-m room, dispersing completely. The site safety officer would probably:

    ○ A.   order the room evacuated of people and fully ventilated

    ○ B.   allow people to continue working for brief periods

    ○ C.   allow work to continue if everyone is wearing a self-contained breathing apparatus

    ○ D.   allow work to continue while the room is being ventilated

97.   The ignition hazard must be reduced for a vessel containing a liquid with a combustive vapor (potential concentrations between the LFL and UFL expected). To most effectively reduce the possibility of ignition you should:

    ○ A.   increase operating temperature 10%

    ○ B.   increase operating pressure 10%

    ○ C.   pad (purge) the vessel with an inert gas

    ○ D.   insulate the vessel exterior

98.   Violations of the Rules of Professional Conduct should be reported to the:

    ○ A.   local chapter of the professional engineers association in the county and state in which the violations occurred

    ○ B.   state chapter of the professional engineers association in the state in which the violations occurred

    ○ C.   office of the attorney in the county and state in which the violations occurred

    ○ D.   board of registration in the state in which the violations occurred

99. As a professional engineer originally licensed 30 years ago, you are asked to evaluate a newly developed computerized control system for a public transportation system. You may accept this project if:

- ○ A. you are competent in the area of modern control systems
- ○ B. your professional engineering license has not lapsed
- ○ C. your original area of specialization was in transportation systems
- ○ D. you have regularly attended meetings of a professional engineering society

100. In the United States, which of the following most directly affects public health and safety with regard to electrical hazards?

- ○ A. NCEES Rules of Professional Conduct
- ○ B. Code of ethics from the Institute of Electrical and Electronics Engineers (IEEE)
- ○ C. Code of ethics from the National Society of Professional Engineers (NSPE)
- ○ D. *National Electrical Code* from the National Fire Protection Association

SOLUTIONS

FE CHEMICAL SOLUTIONS

Detailed solutions for each
question begin on the next page.

1	A	26	A	51	B	76	D
2	B	27	B	52	D	77	A
3	B	28	A	53	C	78	B
4	D	29	D	54	A	79	C
5	see solution	30	C	55	A	80	C
6	see solution	31	D	56	D	81	A
7	B	32	see solution	57	A	82	B
8	A	33	C	58	A	83	B
9	B	34	B	59	see solution	84	see solution
10	C	35	A	60	A	85	B
11	C	36	see solution	61	C	86	A
12	B	37	C	62	see solution	87	A
13	C	38	B	63	C	88	B
14	A	39	B	64	C	89	A
15	C	40	B	65	B	90	B
16	B, C, D, F	41	see solution	66	B	91	D
17	B	42	C	67	B	92	A
18	D	43	D	68	C	93	C
19	C3, C4	44	C	69	B	94	A, B, C, E, G
20	C	45	D	70	see solution	95	B
21	A	46	B	71	D	96	A
22	D	47	D	72	A	97	C
23	C	48	D	73	C	98	D
24	714–715	49	C	74	C	99	A
25	C	50	D	75	C	100	D

FE CHEMICAL SOLUTIONS

1. Refer to the Straight Line section in the Mathematics chapter of the *FE Reference Handbook*.

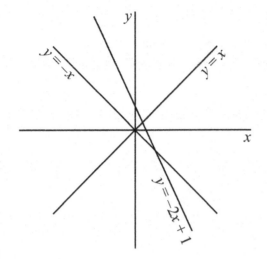

$y = -x$
$y = x$
$y = -2x + 1$

From graph one, the intersection is at $(0, 0)$, so Options C and D are incorrect.

Also, the second intersection is at $(1, -1)$, so the vertices are at $(0, 0)$, $\left(\frac{1}{3}, \frac{1}{3}\right)$, $(1, -1)$.

THE CORRECT ANSWER IS: A

2. Refer to the Differential Equations section in the Mathematics chapter of the *FE Reference Handbook*.

The characteristic equation for a first-order linear homogeneous differential equation is $r + 5 = 0$, which has a root at $r = -5$.

The form of the solution is then:
$y = Ce^{-\alpha t}$ where $\alpha = a$ and $\quad a = 5$ for this problem

C is determined from the boundary condition.

$1 = Ce^{-5(0)}$
$C = 1$

Then, $y = e^{-5t}$

THE CORRECT ANSWER IS: B

3. Refer to the Numerical Integration section in the Mathematics chapter of the *FE Reference Handbook*.

$$\text{Area} = \frac{0.5}{2}\left[0^2 + 2(0.5)^2 + 2(1.0)^2 + 2(1.5)^2 + (2)^2\right] = 2.75$$

THE CORRECT ANSWER IS: B

4. Volume = 100.1 ml, 4 significant figures
   Weight = 100.1 g, 4 significant figures
   Pipette = 1.001 ml 4 significant figures

THE CORRECT ANSWER IS: D

5. Refer to the Differential Calculus section in the Mathematics chapter of the *FE Reference Handbook*.

Point	Location on Curve
$f' = 0$	A, C
$f'' = 0$	B, D
$f'' < 0$	A
$f'' > 0$	C

THE CORRECT ANSWERS ARE SHOWN ABOVE.

6.

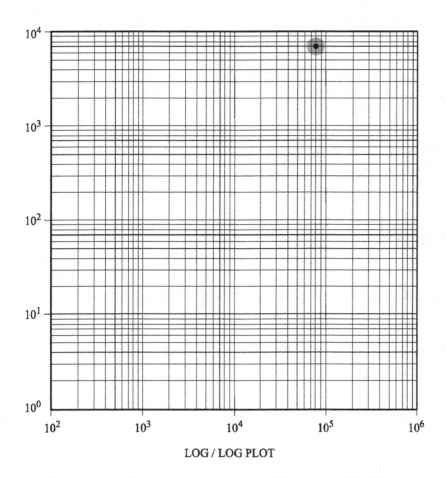

LOG / LOG PLOT

THE CORRECT ANSWER IS SHOWN ON THE GRAPH.

7.   Refer to the Engineering Probability and Statistics chapter of the *FE Reference Handbook.*

Binomial distribution
$p = 0.5$ (chance of getting a head)
$q = 0.5$ (chance of not getting a head)
$n = 10$ (number of trials)
$x = 4$ (number of heads)

$$P_{10}(4) = \frac{10!}{4!6!}(0.5^4)(0.5^6) = \frac{(10)(9)(8)(7)}{(4)(3)(2)(1)}(0.5)^{10}$$

$$= 0.2051$$

THE CORRECT ANSWER IS: B

8. Calculate the distance from mean:
    $8 - 15.5 = 7.5$

    Determine how many standard deviations distance represents:
    $\dfrac{7.5}{2.5} = 3$ standard deviations

    From the Unit Normal Distribution table in the Engineering Probability and Statistics chapter of the *FE Reference Handbook.*

    For $x = 3$, $R(x) = 0.0013$

    THE CORRECT ANSWER IS: A

9. Refer to the Dispersion, Mean, Median, and Mode Values section in the Engineering Probability and Statistics chapter of the *FE Reference Handbook.*

x	$x - \bar{x}$	$(x - \bar{x})^2$
1	−3	9
4	0	0
7	3	9
$\sum = 12$		$\sum = 18$

    $\bar{X} = \dfrac{12}{3} = 4$

    $\sigma = \sqrt{\dfrac{18}{3}} = \sqrt{6}$

    THE CORRECT ANSWER IS: B

10. Refer to the First-Order Control System Models section in the Instrumentation, Measurement, and Controls chapter of the *FE Reference Handbook*.

$$y(t) = y_0 e^{-t/\tau} + KM\left(1 - e^{-t/\tau}\right)$$

$$0.999 \quad = 1 - e^{-t/2.5}$$

$$-0.001 \quad = -e^{-t/2.5}$$

$$0.001 \quad = e^{-t/2.5}$$

Taking natural log both sides

$$-6.908 = -T/2.5$$

$$T = (6.908)(2.5) = 17.3 \text{ minutes}$$

THE CORRECT ANSWER IS: C

11. The upper pin connection has two force reactions. The lower surface supports the member with a normal force.

THE CORRECT ANSWER IS: C

12. Refer to the Resistors in Series and Parallel section in the Electrical and Computer chapter of the *FE Reference Handbook.*

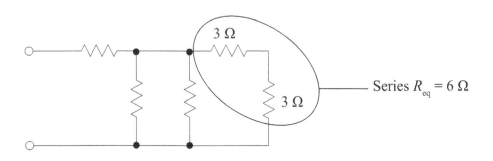

Series $R_{eq} = 6\ \Omega$

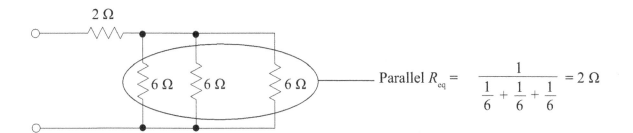

Parallel $R_{eq} = \dfrac{1}{\dfrac{1}{6} + \dfrac{1}{6} + \dfrac{1}{6}} = 2\ \Omega$

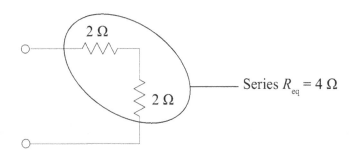

Series $R_{eq} = 4\ \Omega$

THE CORRECT ANSWER IS: B

13. $\sum$ voltages $= 50 - 25 = 25$

$\sum$ resistances $= 10 + 24 + 16 = 50$

$I = \dfrac{25}{50} = 0.5$

The direction opposite to arrow $= -0.5$ A

THE CORRECT ANSWER IS: C

FE CHEMICAL SOLUTIONS

14. Refer to the Vectors section in the Mathematics chapter of the *FE Reference Handbook*.

    THE CORRECT ANSWER IS: A

15. From the Uniaxial Loading and Deformation section in the Mechanics of Materials chapter of the *FE Reference Handbook*, the uniaxial deformation is:

    $$\text{Deformation} = \delta = \frac{PL}{AE} = \frac{(5,000)(0.25)}{(1,250 \times 10^{-6})(200 \times 10^9)} = 5.0 \times 10^{-6} \text{ m} = 5.0 \text{ } \mu\text{m}$$

    THE CORRECT ANSWER IS: C

16. Refer to the Relationship Between Hardness and Tensile Strength section in the Mechanics of Materials chapter of the *FE Reference Handbook*.

    By definition, a metal with high hardness has a high tensile and yield strength, as well as strong intermolecular bonding, with high impact, rebound, and scratch resistance strength.

    THE CORRECT ANSWERS ARE: B, C, D, AND F

17. Refer to the Corrosion section in the Mechanics of Materials chapter of the *FE Reference Handbook*. Aluminum is anodic relative to copper and therefore will corrode to protect the copper.

    THE CORRECT ANSWER IS: B

18. Refer to the Amorphous Materials section in the Mechanics of Materials chapter of the *FE Reference Handbook*. By definition, amorphous materials do not have a crystal structure.

    THE CORRECT ANSWER IS: D

19. Elements in C3 (iron group) and C4 (boron group) contain elements that could have +3 or –3 charge.

    THE CORRECT ANSWERS ARE: C3, C4

20. The double replacement reaction is as follows: $AgNO_3 + HCl \rightarrow AgCl\downarrow + HNO_3$. The reaction products are silver chloride and nitric acid.

THE CORRECT ANSWER IS: C

21. Refer to the Acids, Bases, and pH (aqueous solutions) section in the Chemistry chapter of the *FE Reference Handbook*.

$pH = 2 = -\log [H^+]$

$[H^+] = 10^{-2}$ moles/L

Assuming complete dissociation of the HCl:

Moles HCl $= (10^{-2}$ moles/L$)(1$ L$) = (V)(6.0$ moles/L$)$

$V = 0.00167$ L $= 1.67$ mL

THE CORRECT ANSWER IS: A

22. Refer to the table of Important Formulas of Organic Compounds in the Chemistry chapter of the *FE Reference Handbook*.

The ending "ane" in dodecane means that it is an aliphatic that contains no double bonds. The name dodecane means it contains 12 carbon atoms. Each carbon has two hydrogen atoms attached, except the two terminal carbons, which have three hydrogen atoms.

THE CORRECT ANSWER IS: D

23. Examinees should be familiar with these concepts. The correct answer is atomic adsorption unit.

THE CORRECT ANSWER IS: C

24.

$$\underbrace{C_{60}H_{94}O_{38}N}_{1,433} + 18\,H_2O \rightarrow \underbrace{32\,CH_4}_{(32)(16)=512} + 28\,CO_2 + NH_3$$

$$CH_4 \text{ pounds} = 2,000 \text{ pounds} \left(\frac{512}{1,433}\right) = 714 - 715 \text{ pounds}$$

THE CORRECT ANSWER IS: 714–715

25. The yeast produces alcohol during grape juice fermentation and releases carbon dioxide. The pressure release valves prevent overpressurization of the tanks.

THE CORRECT ANSWER IS: C

26. Refer to specific volumes on the steam tables in the *FE Reference Handbook*.

Density at 25°C is 1/0.001003 = 997.
Density at 5°C is 1/0.001000 = 1,000.
997/1,000 = 0.997

THE CORRECT ANSWER IS: A

27. Refer to the Fluid Flow Characterization section in the Fluid Mechanics section of the *FE Reference Handbook*.

$Re = vD/v = (0.52 \text{ m/s}) \times (1.25 \text{ cm}) / (0.000001306 \text{ m}^2/\text{s}) (100 \text{ cm/m}) = 4,977 \text{ or } {\sim}5,000$

v = kinematic viscosity, which for water at 10°C is 0.000001306 m^2/s, as shown on the Properties of Water table (SI) in the Fluid Mechanics chapter of the *FE Reference Handbook*.

The Reynolds number for this water flow is ~5,000, which would be considered transitional flow.

Re < 2,100 is laminar; 2,100 < Re < 10,000 is transitional; and Re > 10,000 is turbulent.

THE CORRECT ANSWER IS: B

FE CHEMICAL SOLUTIONS

28. Refer to the Jet Propulsion section in the Fluid Mechanics chapter of the *FE Reference Handbook.*

$$v = \sqrt{2gh} = \sqrt{2 \times 9.81 \times 3} = 7.67 \text{ m/s}$$

THE CORRECT ANSWER IS: A

29. Thermal conductivity is a measure of the ability of a material to transmit thermal energy by conduction. The mass diffusivity is a measure of the relative rate at which one species moves through another by diffusion. The heat capacity is a measure of the amount of thermal energy required to increase the temperature of a fixed mass of material. The viscosity is a measure of how easily a fluid flows under a shear stress. Therefore, viscosity is a fluid flow characteristic.

THE CORRECT ANSWER IS: D

30. Refer to the Fluid Flow Characterization section in the Fluid Mechanics chapter of the *FE Reference Handbook.*

$$V = V_{\max}\left[1 - \left(\frac{r}{R}\right)^2\right]$$

$$V = 10\left[1 - \left(\frac{80}{100}\right)^2\right]$$

$$V = 3.6 \text{ m/s}$$

THE CORRECT ANSWER IS: C

31.   Refer to the Fluid Flow Measurement section in the Fluid Mechanics section of the *FE Reference Handbook.*

$$h = \frac{v^2}{2g} = \frac{(2)^2 \, m^2/s^2}{2(9.8) \, m/s^2} = 0.2 \, m$$

THE CORRECT ANSWER IS: D

32.   The point that corresponds to 50 ft head and 70 gpm means both pumps together would be pumping 140 gpm, which matches the head and capacity for the line curve.

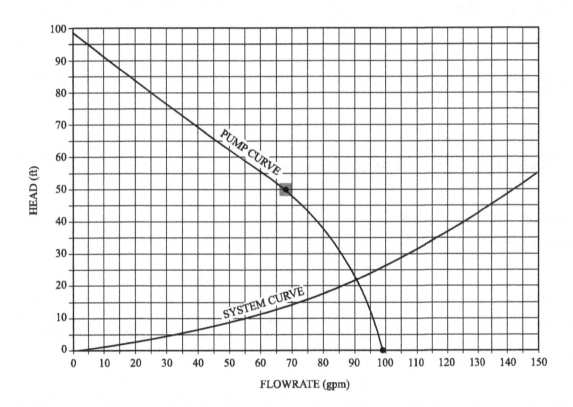

THE CORRECT ANSWER IS SHOWN ON THE FIGURE.

33. Refer to the Compressible Flow section in the Fluid Mechanics chapter of the *FE Reference Handbook.*

Examinees should recognize that the density of the gas will change as the pressure decreases down the pipeline. Compressible flow is characterized by a changing density. Inviscid flow occurs when the fluid has zero viscosity, which is not the case for real fluids. Viscous flow occurs for fluids with moderate to high viscosities, which is not the case for gases at moderate pressures and temperatures.

THE CORRECT ANSWER IS: C

34. Refer to the Ideal Gas section in the Thermodynamics chapter of the *FE Reference Handbook.*

Use the ideal gas formula:

$$PV = mRT$$

$$P = \frac{mRT}{V}$$

$$R = \frac{\overline{R}}{m} = \frac{8,314 \text{ J}}{\text{kmol} \cdot \text{K}} \frac{\text{kmol}}{28 \text{ kg}} = 297 \frac{\text{J}}{\text{kg} \cdot \text{K}}$$

$$P = \frac{(100 \text{ kg})\left(297 \frac{\text{J}}{\text{kg} \cdot \text{K}}\right)(343 \text{ K})}{100 \text{ m}^3}$$

$$= 102,000 \frac{\text{J}}{\text{m}^3}$$

$$= 102,000 \frac{\text{N} \cdot \text{m}}{\text{m}^3}$$

$$= 102,000 \frac{\text{N}}{\text{m}^2}$$

$$= 102 \text{ kPa}$$

THE CORRECT ANSWER IS: B

35. Refer to the P-*h* diagram for Refrigerant HFC-134a in the Thermodynamics chapter of the *FE Reference Handbook*.

The enthalpy at 0.1 quality and 20°C = 250 kJ/kg.

The enthalpy at saturated liquid and 20°C = 410 kJ/kg.

410 – 250 = 170 kJ/kg

THE CORRECT ANSWER IS: A

36. An azeotrope is a condition where the vapor and liquid compositions of a mixture of components are the same. In Options A and D, the vapor and equilibrium liquid compositions are different at all compositions except for the pure species. In Option B and C, there is one mixture composition where the vapor and liquid compositions are equal.

THE CORRECT ANSWERS ARE SHOWN ABOVE.

37. Refer to the Closed Thermodynamic System section in the Thermodynamics chapter of the *FE Reference Handbook*.

$w = P \Delta V$

$w = (100)(1,000 - 500) = (100)(500) = 50,000 \text{ kPa·L}$

$$50,000 \text{ kPa·L} \left(\frac{1 \text{ m}^3}{1,000 \text{ L}} \right) \left(\frac{1,000 \text{ Pa}}{1 \text{ kPa}} \right) \left(\frac{N / m^2}{1 \text{ Pa}} \right)$$

$= 50,000 \text{ N·m}$

$= 50,000 \text{ J}$

$= 50 \text{ kJ}$

THE CORRECT ANSWER IS: C

38. Refer to the Raoult's Law for Vapor-Liquid Equilibrium section in the Thermodynamics chapter of the *FE Reference Handbook*.

Use Raoult's Law, in which $P_{\text{bubble}} = \sum x_i P_i^*$

So, 16.9*0.12 + 12.4*0.34 + 2.8*0.22 + 0.93*0.32 = 7.1576 kPa ≈ 7.2 kPa

THE CORRECT ANSWER IS: B

FE CHEMICAL SOLUTIONS

39. Refer to the Steady-Flow Systems section in the Thermodynamics chapter of the *FE Reference Handbook*.

    Flow through an insulated valve closely follows a throttling process. A throttling process is at constant enthalpy.

    THE CORRECT ANSWER IS: B

40. Refer to the Thermodynamics chapter of the *FE Reference Handbook*. The definition of relative humidity is $\phi = P_v / P_g$ = vapor pressure/saturation pressure

    THE CORRECT ANSWER IS: B

Copyright © 2020 by NCEES 74

41. Refer to the Binary Phase diagrams in the Material Science/Structure of Matter chapter of the *FE Reference Handbook*.

The eutectic composition is the point at which the liquid phase transforms directly to two solid phases. For the Ag-Cu phase diagram, the $L \rightarrow \alpha + \beta$ occurs only at 28.1% Cu and 71.9% Ag.

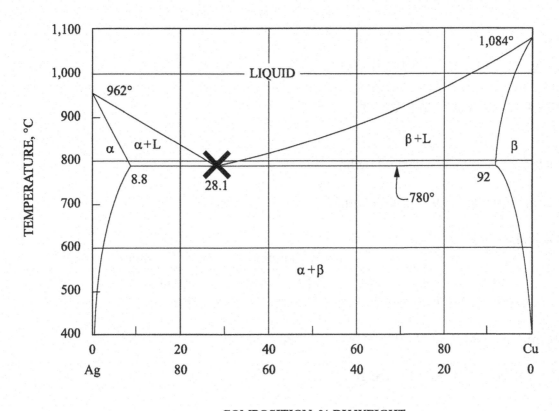

THE CORRECT ANSWER IS MARKED WITH AN X ABOVE.

42. Basis: 100 kg of residue

$$M_{CaCO_3} = 8.3 \text{ kg CaSO}_4 \left(\frac{\text{kmol CaSO}_4}{136.15 \text{ kg CaSO}_4} \right) \left(\frac{1 \text{ kmol CaCO}_3}{1 \text{ kmol CaSO}_4} \right) \left(\frac{100.09 \text{ kg CaCO}_3}{\text{kmol CaCO}_3} \right) = 6.1 \text{ kg}$$

$$M_{MgCO_3} = (5) \left(\frac{84.32}{120.38} \right) = 3.5 \text{ kg}$$

$$M_{inert} = 0.6 \text{ kg}$$

$$M_{dry\ mix} = 6.10 + 3.50 + 0.60 = 10.2 \text{ kg}$$

THE CORRECT ANSWER IS: C

43. NaOH in $= 90{,}000 \times 0.1 = 9{,}000$ kg/hr

Water in $= 90{,}000 \times 0.9 = 81{,}000$ kg/hr

NaOH balance yields

$$\text{Flow of 50\% NaOH} = 9{,}000 \frac{\text{kg NaOH}}{\text{hr}} \times \frac{\text{kg solution}}{0.5 \text{ kg NaOH}} = \frac{18{,}000 \text{ kg solution}}{\text{hr}}$$

Water out in 50% NaOH solution $= 18{,}000 - 9{,}000 = 9{,}000$ kg/hr

Vapor from Effect III $= 81{,}000 - 9{,}000 - 26{,}870 - 24{,}000 = 21{,}130$ kg/hr

THE CORRECT ANSWER IS: D

44. Refer to the steam tables in the Thermodynamics chapter of the *FE Reference Handbook*. h_{fg} of steam at 150°C is 2,114.3 kJ/kg.

$$225 \text{ kW} \times \frac{\text{kJ}}{\text{kW} \cdot \text{s}} \times \frac{1 \text{ kg}}{2{,}114.3 \text{ kJ}} = 0.106 \text{ kg/s}$$

THE CORRECT ANSWER IS: C

45. Refer to the Mass Transfer section in the Chemical Engineering chapter of the *FE Reference Handbook*. A figure of a distillation column is provided.

Overall mass balance on column $Fx_{B,F} = Dx_{B,D} + Bx_{B,B}$

THE CORRECT ANSWER IS: D

46. The unsteady-state energy balance of the liquid batch (rate of accumulation = rate of heat transfer) is the origin of the differential equation

$$mc\frac{dT}{dt} = UA(T_S - T)$$

This relation makes use of Newton's law of cooling in the Basic Heat-Transfer Rate Relations section in the Heat Transfer chapter of the FE Reference Handbook.

THE CORRECT ANSWER IS: B

47. Looking at the overall system, where Y's are mole fractions:

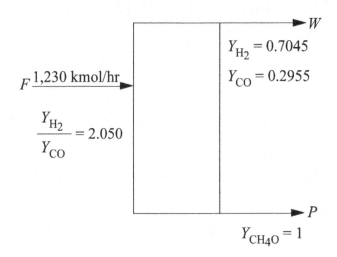

Since $Y_{H_2} + Y_{CO} = 1$ in the feed, $2.050\,Y_{CO} + Y_{CO} = 1$

$\therefore Y_{CO} = 0.3279$ and $Y_{H_2} = 0.6721$ in feed

$\dot{n}_{CO} = (1{,}230)(0.3279) = 403.3$ $\qquad \dot{n}_{H_2} = (1{,}230)(0.6721) = 826.7$ kmol/hr in feed

Solve in two ways.

47. **(Continued)**

Method 1 — Molecular Balance

$CO + 2H_2 \rightarrow CH_4O$

let x kmol/hr of CO react

Species	In	Change	Out	
CO	403.3	$-x$	$403.3 - x$	} Stream W
H_2	826.7	$-2x$	$826.7 - 2x$	
CH_4O	—	$+x$	$+x$	Stream P

From the information in the stoichiometric table, the mole fraction of H_2 in Stream W is

$\dfrac{826.7 - 2x}{1,230 - 3x}$, but this must equal 0.7045.

$\therefore x = 351\dfrac{\text{kmol}}{\text{hr}}$ and $f = \dfrac{351\dfrac{\text{kmol}}{\text{hr}}\text{CO reacted}}{403.3\dfrac{\text{kmol}}{\text{hr}}\text{CO fed}} = 0.87$

Method 2— Atomic Balance

Atomic H balance
$(2)(826.7) = 4\,P + (0.7045)(2)W$

Solve for P and W.

Atomic C balance
$403.3 = P + 0.2955\,W$

$P = 351\dfrac{\text{kmol}}{\text{hr}}$ $W = 177\dfrac{\text{kmol}}{\text{hr}}$

$f = \dfrac{\text{CO reacted}}{\text{CO fed}} = \dfrac{351}{403.3} = 0.87 \text{ or } 87\%$

THE CORRECT ANSWER IS: D

48. Refer to the Combustion Processes section in the Thermodynamics chapter of the *FE Reference Handbook*.

Propane is burned with oxygen according to the following reaction:

$C_3H_8 + 5\ O_2 \rightarrow 3\ CO_2 + 4\ H_2O$

Since there are x moles of air (21% oxygen) furnished, if 1 mole of propane is burned, the O_2 remaining will be:

$0.21x - 5$

THE CORRECT ANSWER IS: D

49. Refer to the Combustion Processes section in the Thermodynamics chapter of the *FE Reference Handbook*.

A nitrogen balance ties the flue gas to the air.

N_2 in the flue gas = (100 kmol flue gas)(0.844 kmol N_2/kmol flue gas)

$\qquad\qquad = 84.4$ kmol N_2

N_2 in air = (Y kmol air)(0.79 kmol N_2/kmol air) = N_2 in flue gas

$Y = 84.4$ kmol N_2/0.79 = 107 kmol air

THE CORRECT ANSWER IS: C

50. Refer to the Heat Exchangers section in the Heat Transfer chapter of the *FE Reference Handbook*.

First, determine the final volume of 19 wt% NaOH after dilution with water:

$$500\,\frac{kg}{hr} \times 50\ wt\% = \frac{250\ kg}{hr}\ NaOH \qquad\qquad \frac{\dfrac{250\ kg}{hr}\ NaOH}{19\%} = 1{,}316\,\frac{kg}{hr}\ of\ 19wt\%\ NaOH$$

Second, determine the heat removal rate:

$$\dot{Q} = \dot{m}C_p\Delta T = \left(1{,}316\,\frac{kg}{hr}\right) \times \left(\frac{3.77\,kJ}{kgK}\right) \times 20K = 99{,}226\ kJ/hr$$

THE CORRECT ANSWER IS: D

51. The amount of moisture in the feed is:
75 tph × 9.3% moisture = 6.98 tph

Solids in feed is:
75 tph – 6.98 tph = 68.02 tph

At steady-state, Incoming solids in feed = Exiting solids in product

68.5 tph product – 68.02 tph solids entering = 0.48 tph moisture remaining in product

$$\text{Final Product Moisture} = \frac{0.48 \text{ tph moisture}}{68.5 \text{ tph dried product}} \times 100\% = 0.70\% \text{ moisture}$$

THE CORRECT ANSWER IS: B

52. Refer to the Conduction Through a Plane Wall section in the Heat Transfer chapter of the *FE Reference Handbook*.

Basis: 1 m² of surface

Heat loss, $Q = h\Delta T$
$= (12)(45 - 30) = 180 \text{ W/m}^2$

Loss through insulation
$$\frac{Q}{A} = -k \frac{\Delta T}{L} = 180$$
$$-\frac{0.035(45 - 200)}{L} = 180$$
$$L = 0.030 \text{ m}$$

THE CORRECT ANSWER IS: D

FE CHEMICAL SOLUTIONS

53. Refer to the Convection section in the Heat Transfer chapter of the *FE Reference Handbook*.

A 100% increase in the flow rate doubles the velocity and increases the Reynolds number by a factor of 2. Thus:

$$\frac{h_{new}}{h_{old}} = \left(\frac{Re_{new}}{Re_{old}}\right)^{0.8} = (2)^{0.8} = 1.7$$

THE CORRECT ANSWER IS: C

54. Refer to the Heat Exchangers section in the Heat Transfer chapter of the *FE Reference Handbook*.

Method A:

$$A_o = 54(1.8)(0.015)\pi = 4.58\,\text{m}^2$$

$$U_o = \frac{Q}{A\,\Delta T_{lm}}$$

$$= \frac{(4{,}184\,\text{J/K})(60°C - 30°C)(1\,\text{kg/s})}{(4.58\,\text{m}^2)(19.6\,\text{K})}$$

$$= 1{,}398.3\,\text{J}/\left(\text{m}^2{\cdot}\text{s}{\cdot}\text{K}\right)$$

$$= 1{,}398\,\text{W}/\left(\text{m}^2{\cdot}\text{K}\right)$$

Method B:

$$\frac{1}{UA_o} = \frac{1}{h_i A_i} + \frac{1}{h_o A_o}$$

$$A_o = \pi D_o L$$

$$A_i = \pi D_i L$$

$$\frac{1}{UD_o} = \frac{1}{h_i D_i} + \frac{1}{h_o D_o}$$

$$\frac{1}{0.015\,U} = \frac{1}{(8{,}700)(0.012)} + \frac{1}{(1{,}750)(0.015)}$$

$$U = 1{,}398\,\text{W}/\left(\text{m}^2{\cdot}\text{K}\right)$$

THE CORRECT ANSWER IS: A

55. Refer to the Net Energy Exchange by Radiation Between Two Bodies section in the Heat Transfer chapter of the *FE Reference Handbook*.

Surface area of sphere:

$$A = \pi d^2 = \pi \left(\frac{50}{100}\right)^2 = 0.785\,\text{m}^2$$

Temperatures C → K
22°C → 295.15 = T_i
75°C → 348.15 = T_∞

Solve for emissivity:

$$\varepsilon = \frac{\dot{Q}}{\sigma A\left(T_i^4 - T_\infty^4\right)}$$

$$= \frac{73\,\text{W}}{\left(5.67\times10^{-8}\,\frac{\text{W}}{\text{m}^2\cdot\text{K}^4}\right)\left(0.785\,\text{m}^2\right)\left(348\,\text{K}^4 - 295\,\text{K}^4\right)}$$

$$= 0.23$$

The resultant emissivity, ε, is 0.23, which coordinates with galvanized steel.

THE CORRECT ANSWER IS: A

56. Refer to the Heat Exchangers section in the Heat Transfer chapter of the *FE Reference Handbook*.

R being the inverse of U would have units that are time × area × temperature per energy.

THE CORRECT ANSWER IS: D

57. Refer to the Transient Conduction Using Lumped Capacitance Model section in the Heat Transfer chapter of the *FE Reference Handbook.*

$$\dot{Q} = \dot{m}C_p\Delta T$$

$$= 7{,}500\,\frac{kg}{min} \times 1.007\,\frac{kJ}{kg{\cdot}K} \times (90-10)\,K \times 1{,}000\,\frac{J}{kJ} \times \frac{min}{60\ sec}$$

$$= 1.01 \times 10^7\ W$$

THE CORRECT ANSWER IS: A

58. Refer to the Noncircular Ducts section in the Heat Transfer chapter of the *FE Reference Handbook.*

$$D_H = \frac{4A}{P} = \frac{(4)(a)(b)}{2a+2b} = \frac{2ab}{a+b}$$

$$D_H = \frac{(2)(10\ mm)(4\ mm)}{10\ mm + 4\ mm} = \frac{80\ mm^2}{14\ mm} = 5.7\ mm$$

THE CORRECT ANSWER IS: A

59. TEMPERATURE PROFILES

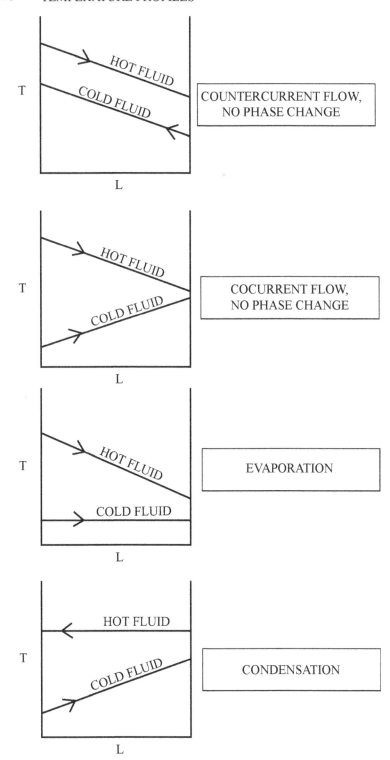

60. The Dimensionless Group equation (Sherwood) is given in the Chemical Engineering section of the *FE Reference Handbook*.

$$\frac{D_m D}{D_m} = 0.023 \left(\frac{DV\rho}{\mu}\right)^{0.8} \left(\frac{\mu}{\rho D_m}\right)^{1/3}$$

Using the definitions of the Reynolds and Schmidt numbers, the following form of the equation is obtained:

$$\frac{D_m D}{D_m} = 0.023\, Re^{0.8}\, Sc^{1/3}$$

$$\frac{D_m D}{D_m} = 0.023(30,000)^{0.8}\,(6)^{1/3} = 159.52$$

$$D_m = 159.52\,\frac{D_m}{D} = 159.52\,\frac{1\times10^{-5}\,\frac{cm^2}{s}}{5\,cm} = 3.19\times10^{-4}\,\frac{cm}{s} = 3.19\times10^{-4}\,\frac{mol}{cm^2 \cdot s \cdot \frac{mol}{cm^3}}$$

Assume that liquid in contact with the surface of the tube is at equilibrium concentration.

$$\text{Flux} = D_m(C_{surface} - C_{bulk}) = 3.19\times10^{-4}\,\frac{mol}{cm^2 \cdot s \cdot \frac{mol}{cm^3}}\left(2\times10^{-4}\,\frac{mol}{cm^3} - 0\right)$$

$$= 6.38\times10^{-8}\,\frac{mol}{cm^2 \cdot s}\left(\frac{100\ cm}{1\ m}\right)^2 = 6.38\times10^{-4}\ mol/(s \cdot m^2)$$

THE CORRECT ANSWER IS: A

61. Refer to the Mass Transfer section in the Chemical Engineering chapter of the *FE Reference Handbook*. Flux is proportional to concentration difference divided by metal thickness.

$$N = \frac{D_m(C - 0)}{L}$$

$$= \frac{\left(0.3\times10^{-12}\,\frac{m^2}{s}\right)\left(1.50\,\frac{kmol}{m^3}\right)}{2\ mm} \times \frac{1,000\ mm}{m}$$

$$= 2.25\times10^{-10}\ kmol/(m^2 \cdot s)$$

THE CORRECT ANSWER IS: C

62. The Dimensionless Group equation (Sherwood) is given in the Chemical Engineering chapter of the *FE Reference Handbook.*

$$[Sh] = [\ ] = \frac{[k][L]}{D} = \frac{[k][L]}{\left[L^2/t\right]} = \frac{[k]}{[L/t]}$$

$$[k] = [\ ][L/t] = [L/t] = [\text{Linear Velocity}]$$

$$Sh = \frac{[\text{ Mass-Transfer Coefficient }] \times [\text{ Pipe Inner Diameter}]}{[\text{ Diffusion Coefficient }]}$$

Or

$$Sh = \frac{[\text{ Pipe Inner Diameter }] \times [\text{ Mass-Transfer Coefficient }]}{[\text{ Diffusion Coefficient }]}$$

THE CORRECT ANSWERS ARE SHOWN ABOVE.

63. Refer to the Vapor-Liquid Equilibrium (VLE) Diagram in the Chemical Engineering chapter of the *FE Reference Handbook.*

8 trays + reboiler (from McCabe-Thiele diagram)

THE CORRECT ANSWER IS: C

64. Refer to the distillation unit diagram in the Murphree Plate Efficiency section in the Chemical Engineering chapter of the *FE Reference Handbook.*

Feed = bottoms + distillate = 100 kg/hr

From diagram, mole fraction of A in the feed is 47%.

Balance on A gives

$$47 = 0.97\,D + 0.04\,B$$

since $B = 100 - D$

then $D = \dfrac{43}{93} = 46.2$

and $B = 100 - 46.2 = 53.8$

THE CORRECT ANSWER IS: C

65. Refer to the Diffusion Coefficient section in the Materials Science/Structure of Matter chapter of the *FE Reference Handbook*.

$$D = D_{o_e}{}^{-Q/CRT}$$

$$D = \left(1.9 \times 10^{-5}\right)e^{-150,000/\left[(8.31)(773)\right]}$$

$$D = 1.37 \times 10^{-15} \text{ m}^2/\text{s}$$

THE CORRECT ANSWER IS: B

66. Refer to the Distillation section in the Chemical Engineering Chapter of the *FE Reference Handbook*.

THE CORRECT ANSWER IS: B

67. Refer to the ASHRAE psychrometric chart in the Thermodynamics chapter in the *FE Reference Handbook*.

Calculate the humidity: H = 1.2 kg water/50 kg air = 0.024.
Locate the humidity value on the chart.
Follow a horizontal line from the humidity scale over to the saturated air curve.
Drop a vertical line down to the temperature scale to obtain the result.

THE CORRECT ANSWER IS: B

68. 55 tph of slurry at 38% solids contains 20.9 tph of solids and 34.1 tph water.

In the screw conveyor stage, 67% of moisture is removed, or 22.85 tph. That leaves 20.9 tph solids entering the belt filter and 11.25 tph of moisture exiting the screw conveyor (feed to belt filter).

At the belt filter, 89% of the incoming moisture is removed, or 10.02 tph of moisture, leaving 1.24 tph of moisture leaving the belt filter with the 20.9 tph of solids.

Final moisture content is calculated as:

$$\frac{(1.24 \text{ tph moisture})}{(1.24 \text{ tph moisture})+(20.9 \text{ tph solids})} \times 100\% = 5.6\% \text{ moisture in final sludge}$$

THE CORRECT ANSWER IS: C

69. Refer to the Environmental Engineering chapter of the *FE Reference Handbook.*

The electrostatic precipitator, cyclone, and baghouse are all commonly used for gas/solid separations. Centrifuges are used primarily to achieve a liquid/solid separation.

THE CORRECT ANSWER IS: B

70. $\theta = \tan^{-1}(14/24) = 30.3°$

Thus any material with an angle of repose greater than 30.3° will have a height greater than 14 ft. Dry sand, crushed gravel, and wood chips have angles of repose greater than 30.3°.

THE CORRECT ANSWER IS SHOWN ABOVE.

71. Refer to the Second-Order Irreversible Reaction section in the Chemical Engineering chapter of the *FE Reference Handbook.*

$$-\frac{dC_A}{dt} = kC_A^2$$

$$-\frac{dC_A}{C_A^2} = kdt$$

$$\frac{1}{C_A} - \frac{1}{C_{A0}} = kt$$

$$C_{A0} = 25 \text{ mol / L}$$

$$X_A = 0.8 \text{ (conversion)}$$

$$C_A = 25(1-0.8) = 5 \text{ mol/L}$$

$$k = 0.01 \text{ L}/(\text{mol·s})$$

$$t = \left(\frac{1}{5} - \frac{1}{25}\right) \text{L / mol} \times \frac{1}{0.01} \text{ mol·s / L} = 16 \text{ s} = 0.27 \text{ min}$$

THE CORRECT ANSWER IS: D

72. Refer to the First-Order Reversible Reactions section in the Chemical Engineering chapter of the *FE Reference Handbook.*

$$-\ln\left(1-\frac{X_A}{\hat{X}_A}\right) = \frac{M+1}{M+\hat{X}_A}k_1 t$$

$$-\ln\left(1-\frac{0.60}{0.92}\right) = \frac{1.6+1}{1.6+0.92}k_1\left(4\text{ hr}\right)\left(60\frac{\text{min}}{\text{hr}}\right)$$

$$k_1 = 0.0042\text{ min}^{-1}$$

THE CORRECT ANSWER IS: A

73. Refer to the First-Order Reversible Reactions section in the Chemical Engineering chapter of the *FE Reference Handbook.*

THE CORRECT ANSWER IS: C

74. Refer to the Arrhenius equation in the Chemical Engineering chapter of the *FE Reference Handbook.*

Find E_a, activation energy

$$\ln\frac{k_2}{k_1} = \frac{E_a}{R}\left[\frac{1}{T_1} - \frac{1}{T_2}\right]$$

$$E_a = \ln\frac{k_2}{k_1} \times \frac{R}{\left[\dfrac{1}{T_1} - \dfrac{1}{T_2}\right]}$$

$$E_a = \ln\frac{1.1}{0.5} \times \frac{8.314}{\left[\dfrac{1}{313} - \dfrac{1}{343}\right]} = 0.7885 \times \frac{8.314}{0.603195 - 0.002915} = 23,400\ \text{J/mol}$$

@ 100°C

$$\ln\frac{k_{100}}{k_{40}} = \frac{23,400}{8.314}\left[\frac{1}{313} - \frac{1}{373}\right]$$

$$\ln\frac{k_{100}}{0.5} = \frac{23,400}{8.314}\left[0.003195 - 0.002681\right] = 1.4467$$

$$\frac{k_{100}}{0.5} = 4.2489 \qquad k_{100} = 2.124\ \text{sec}^{-1}$$

THE CORRECT ANSWER IS: C

75. Refer to the Chemical Reaction Equilibrium section in the Thermodynamics chapter of the *FE Reference Handbook.*

Convert 80% of A (1 mole)
0.8 (1) = C + B

Selectivity B/C = 9, so
0.8 = C (1 + B/C)
C = 0.08 and B = 0.72

THE CORRECT ANSWER IS: C

76. Refer to the Flow Reactors, Steady State section in the Chemical Engineering chapter of the *FE Reference Handbook.*

$$\tau = \frac{V}{q} = \frac{0.50 \text{ m}^3}{0.20 \text{ m}^3/\text{min}} = 2.5 \text{ min}$$

THE CORRECT ANSWER IS: D

77. Refer to the Definitions section in the Chemistry chapter of the *FE Reference Handbook.*

THE CORRECT ANSWER IS: A

78. Area B shows the FCI Year 2 = 60,000.

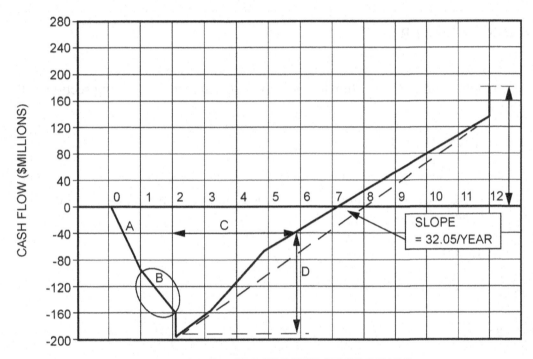

TIME AFTER PROJECT START (YEARS)

THE CORRECT ANSWER IS: B

79. Refer to the table of cash flow equations in the Engineering Economics chapter of the *FE Reference Handbook*.

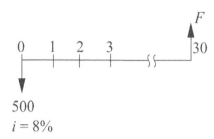

$F = 500(F/P, 8\%, 30)$

$\quad = 500\,(10.0627)$

$\quad = \$5,031$

THE CORRECT ANSWER IS: C

80. Refer to the Classification of Cost Estimates table in the Chemical Engineering section of the *FE Reference Handbook*.

THE CORRECT ANSWER IS: C

81. Refer to the Breakeven Analysis section in the Engineering Economics chapter of the *FE Reference Handbook*.

$\$1.50\,(5,000) = \$7,500$

$\$0.50\,(5,000) = \$2,500$

Annual savings = \$7,500 – \$2,500 = \$5,000

Additional investment = \$15,000 – \$1,000 = \$14,000

Payback = \$14,000/\$5,000 = 2.8 years

THE CORRECT ANSWER IS: A

FE CHEMICAL SOLUTIONS

82. Process stream compositions are shown on process flow diagrams (PFDs), not P&IDs.

    THE CORRECT ANSWER IS: B

83. Refer to the definition of breakeven analysis in the Engineering Economics chapter of the *FE Reference Handbook*.

    THE CORRECT ANSWER IS: B

84. Refer to the Fluid Flow Machinery section in the Fluid Mechanics chapter of the *FE Reference Handbook* for characteristics of centrifugal pumps.

    Impeller diameter = 7 3/4 in.
    Pump = 2 hp
    Efficiency = 72%

    THE CORRECT ANSWERS ARE SHOWN ABOVE.

85. Use the exponent 0.60 from the table of Typical Exponents for Equipment Cost vs. Capacity from the Chemical Engineering chapter of the *FE Reference Handbook*.

    $$\text{Cost of 200-ft}^2 \text{ exchanger} = \$8,700 \,(200/400)^{0.6}$$
    $$= \$8,700 \,(0.660)$$
    $$= \$5,740$$

    THE CORRECT ANSWER IS: B

86. IEEE provides best practices for electrical and electronics applications.

    EPA has administrative responsibility for the Risk Management Plan, which references ASME standards as best practice.

    NFPA provides best practices for fire and overpressure protection.

    THE CORRECT ANSWER IS: A

87. To maximize profitability of the plant, the plant must produce a sellable product that maximizes the daily overall sales margin. That point occurs in the table in Area A, where production is at 400 units per day and the daily sales margin is $23,600.

THE CORRECT ANSWER IS: AREA A

88. Refer to the cash flow equations table in the Engineering Economics chapter of the *FE Reference Handbook*.

The easiest way to solve this problem is to look at the present worth of each alternative.

The present worth values are all given by

P = First Cost + Annual Cost × (P/A, 12%, 8) – Salvage Value × (P/F, 12%, 8)
= First Cost + Annual Cost × 4.9676 – Salvage Value × 0.4039

Then
P(A) = $63,731
P(B) = $63,392
P(C) = $63,901
P(D) = $63,222

The cash flows are all costs, so the two most preferable pieces of equipment, those with the lowest present worth costs, are B and D, and the difference between them is $170.

THE CORRECT ANSWER IS: B

89. Refer to the Control Systems section in the Instrumentation, Measurement, and Control chapter of the *FE Reference Handbook*.

The characteristic equation is:

$$1 + \frac{(0.1\,K_C)}{(s+1)(2s+1)} = 0$$

which simplifies to:

$$0.1\,K_C + 2s^2 + 3s + 1 = 0$$

The Routh array is:

2	$1 + K_C$
3	0
$1 + K_C$	

The system is stable for all positive K_C. Note that this is a second-order process with a proportional controller. With any other stability analysis technique (root locus, phase margin, etc.), the system will be stable for all positive controller gains.

THE CORRECT ANSWER IS: A

90. Refer to the Control Systems section in the Instrumentation, Measurement, and Control chapter of the *FE Reference Handbook*. The figure shows both feedforward control (flow) and feedback control (temperature).

THE CORRECT ANSWER IS: B

91. Refer to the Control Systems section in the Instrumentation, Measurement, and Control chapter of the *FE Reference Handbook*.

$$\frac{C(s)}{R(s)} = \frac{K_c G(s)}{1 + K_c G(s)} \qquad G(s) = \frac{3}{8s+1}$$

$$\frac{C(s)}{R(s)} = \frac{\dfrac{(K_c)(3)}{8s+1}}{1 + \dfrac{(K_c)(3)}{8s+1}} = \frac{\dfrac{3K_c}{8s+1}}{\dfrac{8s+1+3K_c}{8s+1}} = \frac{3K_c}{8s+1+3K_c}$$

THE CORRECT ANSWER IS: D

92. Refer to the Control Systems section in the Instrumentation, Measurement, and Control chapter of the *FE Reference Handbook.*

$C = G_2M + G_2L$

$C = G_2G_1G_C(R - B) + G_2L$

$C = G_2G_1G_CR - G_2G_1G_CHC + G_2L$

$(1 + G_2G_1G_CH)C = G_2G_1G_CR + G_2L$

$C = \dfrac{G_2G_1G_C}{1+G_2G_1G_CH}R + \dfrac{G_2}{1+G_2G_1G_CH}L$

The two transfer functions are:

$$C/R = \frac{G_2G_1G_C}{1+G_2G_1G_CH}$$

$$C/L = \frac{G_2}{1+G_2G_1G_CH}$$

THE CORRECT ANSWER IS: A

93. Refer to the Permissible Noise Exposure (OSHA) section in the Safety chapter of the *FE Reference Handbook.*

Noise dose $= 100 \times (16/32 + 4/8 + 1/2) = 150$. A noise abatement program is required.

THE CORRECT ANSWER IS: C

94. Refer to the Safety Data Sheet (SDS) section in the Safety chapter of the *FE Reference Handbook.*

There is a defined format that all Safety Data Sheets must follow. The format specifies the layout of the document as well the mandatory and optional information that may be included.

Option A is contained in Section 2 of the SDS, Option B is contained in section 5, Option C is contained in section 8, Option E is contained in section 9, and Option G is contained in section 8. An SDS does not contain information about the materials of construction that can be used (Option D) or the chemical reactions that can be used to produce the chemical (Option F).

THE CORRECT ANSWERS ARE: A, B, C, E, G

95. Assume there is very little steam in the tank when it is sealed. It condenses but does not appreciably change the volume of air in the tank. Assume the starting temperature was at least 100°C and cools overnight to 20°C.

$$\frac{P_1V_1}{T_1} = \frac{P_2V_2}{T_2} \qquad P_2 = \frac{P_1V_1}{T_1}\frac{T_2}{V_2} = \frac{P_1 293}{373} = 0.78P_1$$

Storage tanks are not usually vacuum rated, so the reduced pressure would likely collapse it.

THE CORRECT ANSWER IS: B

96. Refer to the Exposure Limits for Selected Compounds section in the Safety chapter of the *FE Reference Handbook.*

$4 \times 4 \times 4 = 64 \text{ m}^3$

$64 \text{ m}^3 \times 188 \text{ mg/m}^3 = 12{,}032 \text{ mg} = 12 \text{ g} =$ allowable workplace exposure

50 g far exceeds the 12 g allowed

THE CORRECT ANSWER IS: A

97. Nitrogen padding is widely practiced and highly effective in preventing unwanted combustion.

THE CORRECT ANSWER IS: C

98. Refer to the Ethics chapter of the *FE Reference Handbook.* Section A.8 in the Rules of Professional Conduct dictates the reporting of violations.

THE CORRECT ANSWER IS: D

99. Refer to the NCEES Rules of Professional Conduct, Section B, in the Ethics chapter of the *FE Reference Handbook.*

THE CORRECT ANSWER IS: A

100. NFPA70 is the *National Electrical Code* put forth by the National Fire Protection Association. It is widely adopted across the United States.

THE CORRECT ANSWER IS: D

**FE EXAM PREPARATION MATERIAL
PUBLISHED BY NCEES**

FE Reference Handbook

FE Practice Exams for all modules:
Chemical
Civil
Electrical and Computer
Environmental
Industrial and Systems
Mechanical
Other Disciplines

For more information about these and other NCEES publications and services,
visit us at www.ncees.org or contact
Client Services at (800) 250-3196.